AUTHORS

ELAINE MEI AOKI	ANNEMARIE SULLIVAN	WILLIAM H. TEALE
VIRGINIA A. ARNOLD	PALINCSAR	JOSEFINA VILLAMIL
JAMES FLOOD	MICHAEL PRIESTLEY	TINAJERO
JAMES V. HOFFMAN	NANCY ROSER	ARNOLD W. WEBB
DIANE LAPP	CARL B. SMITH	PEGGY E. WILLIAMS
MIRIAM MARTINEZ		KAREN D. WOOD

MACMILLAN/McGRAW-HILL SCHOOL PUBLISHING COMPANY

NEW YORK   CHICAGO   COLUMBUS

AUTHORS, CONSULTANTS, AND REVIEWERS

WRITE IDEA! Authors

Elaine Mei Aoki, James Flood, James V. Hoffman, Diane Lapp, Ana Huerta Macias, Miriam Martinez, Ann McCallum, Michael Priestley, Nancy Roser, Carl B. Smith, William Strong, William H. Teale, Charles Temple, Josefina Villamil Tinajero, Arnold W. Webb, Peggy E. Williams

The approach to writing in Macmillan/McGraw-Hill Reading/Language Arts is based on the strategies and approaches to composition and conventions of language in Macmillan/McGraw-Hill's writing-centered language arts program, WRITE IDEA!

Multicultural and Educational Consultants

Alma Flor Ada, Yvonne Beamer, Joyce Buckner, Helen Gillotte, Cheryl Hudson, Narcita Medina, Lorraine Monroe, James R. Murphy, Sylvia Peña, Joseph B. Rubin, Ramon Santiago, Cliff Trafzer, Hai Tran, Esther Lee Yao

Literature Consultants

Ashley Bryan, Joan I. Glazer, Paul Janeczko, Margaret H. Lippert

International Consultants

Edward B. Adams, Barbara Johnson, Raymond L. Marshall

Music and Audio Consultants

John Farrell, Marilyn C. Davidson, Vincent Lawrence, Sarah Pirtle, Susan R. Snyder, Rick and Deborah Witkowski

Teacher Reviewers

Terry Baker, Jane Bauer, James Bedi, Nora Bickel, Vernell Bowen, Donald Cason, Jean Chaney, Carolyn Clark, Alan Cox, Kathryn DesCarpentrie, Carol L. Ellis, Roberta Gale, Brenda Huffman, Erma Inscore, Sharon Kidwell, Elizabeth Love, Isabel Marcus, Elaine McCraney, Michelle Moraros, Earlene Parr, Dr. Richard Potts, Jeanette Pulliam, Michael Rubin, Henrietta Sakamaki, Kathleen Cultron Sanders, Belinda Snow, Dr. Jayne Steubing, Margaret Mary Sulentic, Barbara Tate, Seretta Vincent, Willard Waite, Barbara Wilson, Veronica York

ACKNOWLEDGMENTS

The publisher gratefully acknowledges permission to reprint the following copyrighted material:

"Angel Child, Dragon Child." From ANGEL CHILD, DRAGON CHILD with text by Michele Maria Surat and pictures by Vo-Dinh Mai. Text copyright © 1983 by Carnival Press, Inc. Illustrations copyright © 1983 by Vo-Dinh Mai. Permission to reprint the art from Vo-Dinh Mai. Every effort has been made to find the other copyright holder.

"April Rain Song" from THE DREAM KEEPER by Langston Hughes. Copyright 1932 by Alfred A. Knopf, Inc. and renewed 1960 by Langston Hughes. Reprinted by permission of the publisher.

"Beginning on Paper" from SOMEBODY SPILLED THE SKY by Ruth Krauss. Copyright © 1976, 1979 by Ruth Krauss. Used by permission of the author.

"The Best Friends Club." This is the entire text and nineteen illustrations from THE BEST FRIENDS CLUB by Elizabeth Winthrop with illustrations by Martha Weston. Text copyright © 1989 by Elizabeth Winthrop with illustrations by Martha Weston. Text copyright © 1989 by Elizabeth Winthrop. Illustrations copyright © 1989 by Martha Weston. Reprinted by permission of William Morrow and Company, Inc./Publishers, New York.

"Best Wishes, Ed" from WINSTON, NEWTON, ELTON, AND ED by James Stevenson. Copyright © 1978 by James Stevenson. Reprinted by permission of William Morrow and Company, Inc./Publishers, New York.

"Colores de Caracol" ("The rainbow showing") from VERY VERY SHORT NATURE POEMS by Ernesto Galarza. Copyright ©1972 by Ernesto Galarza. Reprinted by permission of Mrs. Mae Galarza.

"Come a Tide." From COME A TIDE by George Ella Lyon with illustrations by Stephen Gammell. Text copyright © 1990 by George Ella Lyon. Illustrations copyright © 1990 by Stephen Gammell. All rights reserved. Reprinted by permission of Orchard Books, New York.

Cover illustration of COULD BE WORSE! by James Stevenson. Copyright © 1977 by James Stevenson. By permission of William Morrow & Company, Inc./Publishers, New York.

"A Curve in the River" from MORE STORIES JULIAN TELLS by Ann Cameron. Illustrated by Ann Strugnell. Text copyright © 1986 by Ann Strugnell. Reprinted by permission of Alfred A. Knopf, Inc.

"DEADLINE! From News to Newspaper." This is the entire work DEAD-LINE! FROM NEWS TO NEWSPAPER by Gail Gibbons. Copyright © 1987 by Gail Gibbons. Reprinted by permission of HarperCollins Publishers.

"Dear Daddy. . ." From DEAR DADDY by Philippe Dupasquier. Copyright © 1985 by Philippe Dupasquier. Reprinted with permission from Bradbury Press, an affiliate of Macmillan, Inc.

"Everett Anderson's Friend." Text of EVERETT ANDERSON'S FRIEND by Lucille Clifton. Copyright © 1976 by Lucille Clifton. Reprinted by permission of Curtis Brown, Ltd. Illustrations by Ann Grifalconi. Illustrations copyright © 1976 by Ann Grifalconi. Reprinted by permission of Henry Holt and Company, Inc.

"Finding a Way" from THERE WAS A PLACE AND OTHER POEMS by Myra Cohn Livingston. Copyright © 1988 by Myra Cohn Livingston. Reprinted by permission of Margaret K. McElderry Books, an imprint of Macmillan Publishing Company.

"Inviting Rippling Waters" by Margaret Bendig is from MIRACLES: POEMS BY CHILDREN OF THE ENGLISH-SPEAKING WORLD. Collected by Richard Lewis. © 1990 Richard Lewis & The Touchstone Center. Used by permission.

"It's Dark in Here" is the text and art of "It's Dark in Here" from WHERE THE SIDEWALK ENDS by Shel Silverstein. Copyright © 1974 by Evil Eye Music, Inc. Reprinted by permission of HarperCollins Publishers.

(continued on page 359)

Macmillan/McGraw-Hill School Division
10 Union Square East
New York, New York 10003

Printed in the United States of America
ISBN 0-02-178757-3 / 2, L.7
   3 4 5 6 7 8 9   RRW   99 98 97 96 95 94 93

To Dr. Jeanne Chall:
My Professor of Reading Education at Harvard University, who continues to inspire my love of reading and learning.

Amy Joanne Lee

To Heath Ryan Gillespie, Cynthia Rylant, and Joseph Cox — for their splashes of love, inspiration, encouragement and wisdom

Cindy Randall
Bob Boltz
Mary Farley Cox

You've Got the Write Idea!

BETTER TOGETHER

water, water everywhere

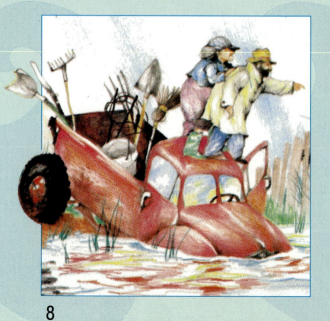

CONTENTS

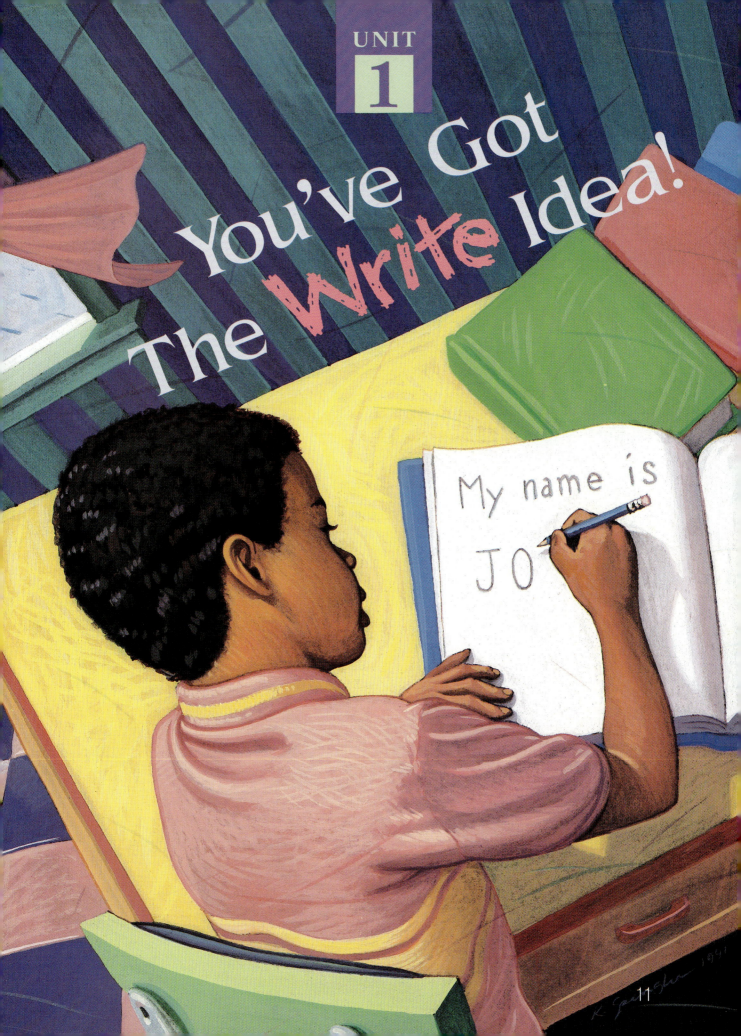

You've Got The *Write* Idea!

My name is

JO

BEGINNING ON PAPER

on paper
I write it
on rain

I write it
on stones
on my boots

on trees
I write it
on the air

on the city
how pretty
I write my name

RUTH KRAUSS

When Philippe Dupasquier moved from France to London, England, he thought about his family in France and wondered what they were doing. "Dear Daddy... came from that," he says. "If you're away from someone you care about, thinking of what they are doing makes you feel less alone."

Mr. Dupasquier lives in the countryside near London. He says, "You are isolated here, so small things that happen are important. You notice the little things like cars in the streets and the changing of the seasons. I watched things around me and put them into *Dear Daddy*... Most of the ideas for the book came from things that happened in my family and from things I saw around me in England."

Air Mail

Mr. John Slater
S. S. Eternity
Jefferson Lines
c/o Frederick Morse Agt.
Hong Kong

Meet
Philippe Dupasquier

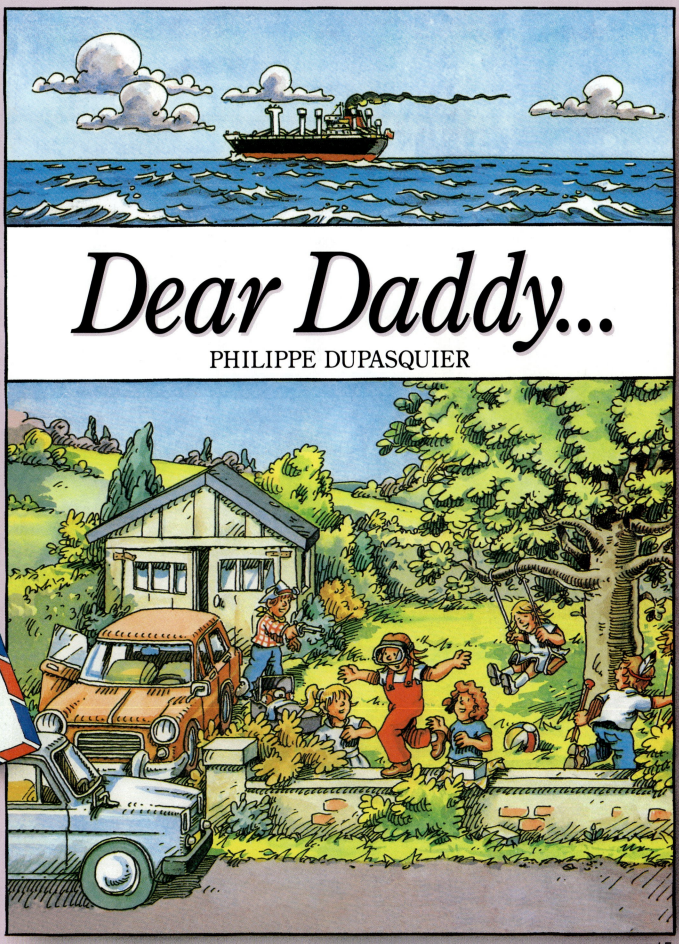

Dear Daddy...

PHILIPPE DUPASQUIER

Dear Daddy,

I think about you lots and lots. Are you all right on your ship? We all miss you.

It's raining all the time at home, so Mommy bought me some red boots. They're great!

Mr. Green the gardener came to trim the hedge today.
Timmy's got a new tooth. He's got six altogether now.

Mommy says he'll soon be walking. I hope you are well.
We think about you all the time.

I had a great birthday party. All my friends came,
except for Jacky—she had chicken-pox. Mommy made
a chocolate cake.

I had lots and lots of presents. My best one was a mask
for looking underwater when we go to the beach.

School has started again. The garden is full of dead leaves.
The teacher showed me on a big map where you are
going on your ship.

She said it was a very long way. I wish you were home again.

It's very cold and Timmy is sick. Dr. Rush came and he looked in Timmy's mouth and listened to his chest with a stethoscope. He said it's not too bad, and Mommy went to buy some medicine.

I liked the postcard you sent us. There's lots of snow
here. Timmy and me made a huge snowman. Mommy
says if I'm good, Santa Claus might bring me a bicycle.
That would be great!

Some men from the music shop brought back the old piano today. They have fixed it. Mommy is very happy.

She's going to teach me how to play it. Then when I'm
big, I'll be a pianist and go around the world just like you.

When you come home, we'll do all sorts of things together.
We can go walking in the woods, and fishing in the pond,
just like we used to . . .

and at night-time, we'll look up at the sky and you can
tell me the story of the little prince who lives on a star.

It's not long till summer and I know we'll soon be all together again.

I think about you every day. Please come home quickly.

Love from Sophie

Write All About It!

Be a Printer!

You can make your own stationery.

Use potatoes to make letters or shapes.

You can use a stencil, too.

Make prints on colorful papers

using paints or inks.

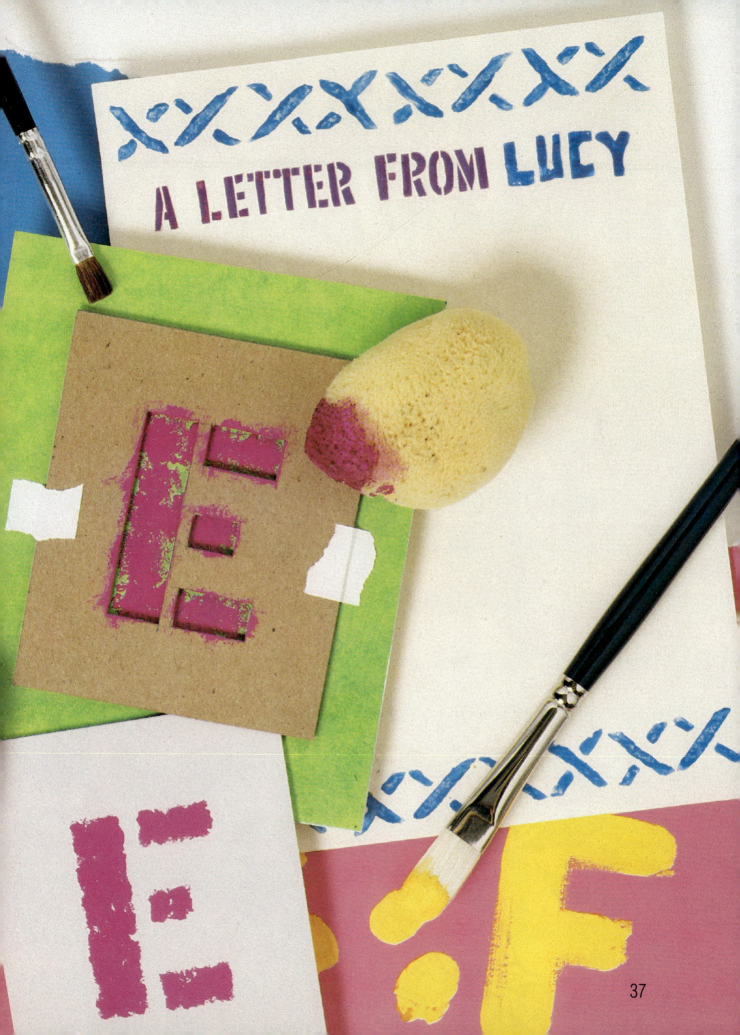

A LETTER FROM LUCY

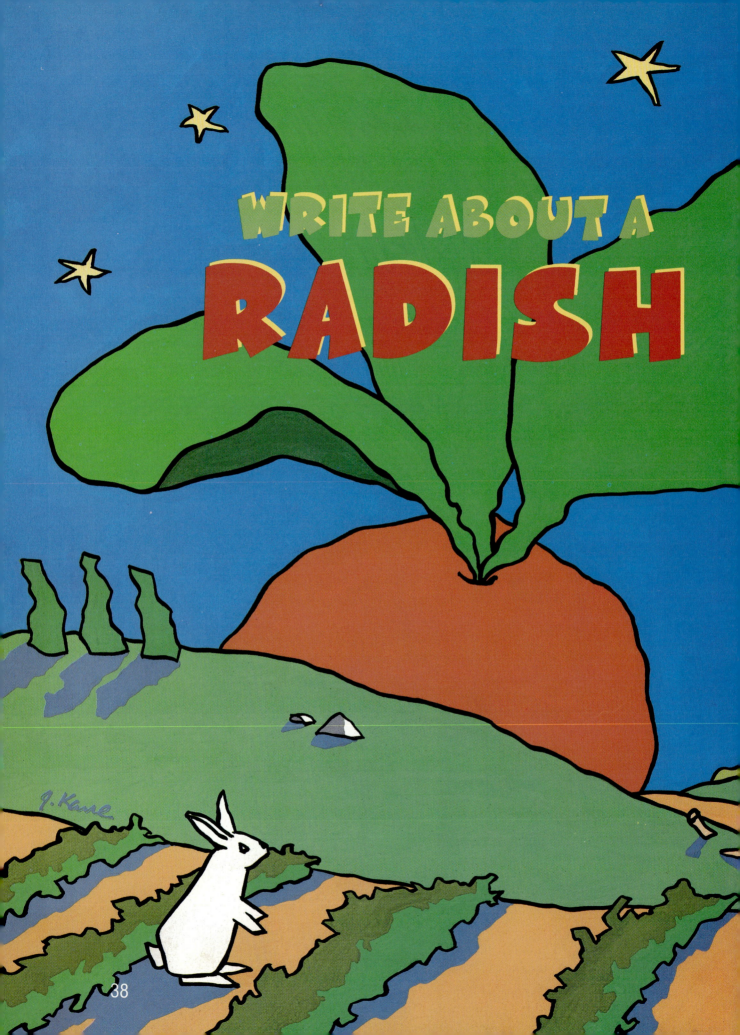

WRITE ABOUT A RADISH

Write about a radish
Too many people write about the moon.

The night is black
The stars are small and high
The clock unwinds its ever-ticking tune
Hills gleam dimly
Distant nighthawks cry.
A radish rises in the waiting sky.

Karla Kuskin

✳ Meet James Stevenson

James Stevenson began writing and drawing as a child. He loved to watch movies and read comic books. He says that both activities influenced the books he writes for children.

He says, "I think that my experience and creative mind have been formed by movies and comic books. I like to write. I like to draw. I like to paint. And in writing picture books I found a way to tell a story without using just words."

When asked if he prefers drawing to writing, he said, "I think that drawing is the more childlike and natural. When you're a little kid, you grab crayons, you don't grab the typewriter. I think drawing is a little more fun than writing, but whether it's more satisfying by the time you're old, I don't know."

BEST WISHES, ED

*by
JAMES STEVENSON

Ed lived on a big island of ice
with Betty, Freddy, Al,
and a lot of other penguins.
Every day they had fun
throwing snowballs
and sliding on the ice.

But they always watched out
for Ernest, the big whale.
Every time he went by...
SPLAT!
Ed and everybody got soaked.

"Watch what you are doing!"
Betty would yell.

But Ernest swam right by.
"Ernest doesn't even notice penguins,"
said Ed.

One night when Ed was asleep,
there was a loud cracking noise.
It sounded like ice breaking.
Ed thought it was a dream.

When Ed woke up in the morning,
he found that the island of ice
had broken in half.
He was all alone
on an island of his own.

Ed's friends got smaller
and smaller
as his island drifted away.
Ed watched until he couldn't
see them anymore.

Then he walked
around his island.
There was nobody on it at all.
At last he came to his
own footprints again.

Some birds flew over.
Ed waved,
but they did not wave back.
"I guess I will be here
the rest of my life," Ed said.
At the end of the day,
he wrote "I GIVE UP"
in big letters in the snow.
Then he went to sleep.

In the morning a tern woke him up.
"Hey," said the tern,
"did you write that thing in the snow?"

"Yes," said Ed.

"Could you write something
for me?" asked the tern.

"I guess so," said Ed.
"What do you want?"

"Tell my friends to meet me
at the blue iceberg," said the tern.
"And sign it 'Talbot.'
That is my name."

Talbot flew away,
and Ed wrote the message.

MEET
TALBOT
AT THE
BLUE
ICEBERG

Pretty soon, Talbot's friends
flew over and read the message.
They waved to Ed,
and Ed waved back.

HAROLD:
YOUR SUPPER IS READY

All day long, birds stopped and asked Ed
to write messages for them.
By the end of the day, the whole island
was covered with messages.
Ed was very tired.

DOROTHY:
MARTHA IS
LOOKING FOR YOU

GEORGE
MARY
IS AT

Talbot landed and gave Ed a fish.
"You are doing a great job,"
said Talbot.
"How come you look so gloomy?"

"I miss my friends
on my old island," said Ed.

"Where is your old island?"
asked Talbot.

"Way over there someplace,"
said Ed.

"Too bad you can't fly," said Talbot.
"You could spot it from the air."

"Well, I can't fly," said Ed.

"It's not very hard," said Talbot.

"It is for penguins," said Ed.

Talbot flew away.
"I guess I will spend the rest
of my life writing messages,"
Ed said to himself.

When Ed got up the next morning,
he found a surprise.

ED - THERE'S
A MESSAGE
FOR YOU!

FOLLOW THE ARROWS

55

SIT HERE AND WAIT → ✕

He followed the arrows
until he came to another message.

He sat down on the X
and waited.

Suddenly there was a great SPLAT!
Ed was soaked.
It was Ernest.
"I understand you are looking
for a ride to that island
with all the penguins on it,"
said Ernest.

"How did you know?" asked Ed.

"Talbot told me," said Ernest.
"Hop aboard."

"Wait one second," said Ed.
"I have to leave a message."

"Well, make it snappy," said Ernest.
"I have other things to do
besides give rides to penguins."

Ed quickly wrote
the message in the snow.

THANK YOU,
TALBOT.
BEST WISHES,
Ed

Then he climbed
on top of Ernest's back.
Ernest gave a couple of
big splashes with his tail,
and then they were racing
across the water.

"Ed is back!" yelled Betty.

"Hooray!" shouted Freddy and Al.

Ed slid off Ernest's back.
"Thanks a lot, Ernest," called Ed.

"That's O.K.," said Ernest.
"Just don't expect a ride every day."

"We're so glad you are back, Ed,"
said Betty.

"We missed you a lot,"
said Freddy and Al.

"I missed you," said Ed.

SPLAT! They were all soaked,
as Ernest swam away.

"Hey," said Betty, "he did it again!"

"Ernest doesn't notice penguins,"
said Freddy.

"Sometimes he does," said Ed.

There was an old pig with a pen

There was an old pig with a pen
Who wrote stories and verse now and then.
To enhance these creations,
He drew illustrations
With brushes, some paints and his pen.

There was an old pig with a pen
Who had finished his work once again.
Then he quietly sat
With his comfortable cat . . .

While he rested his brushes and pen.

Arnold Lobel

Read all

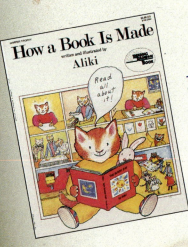

How a Book Is Made
Written and illustrated by Aliki
Harper Trophy, 1988

Many people made this book.
And this is how they did it.

about it!

The Day of Ahmed's Secret

Written by Florence Parry Heide
and Judith Heide Gilliland
illustrated by Ted Lewin
Lothrop, Lee & Shepard, 1990

*"Today I have a secret,
and all day long my secret will be
like a friend to me."*

Dead

From News to

MEET GAIL GIBBONS

"The reason I wrote *Deadline! From News to Newspaper* was to explain how a newspaper is made. I was curious about how people put together a newspaper everyday, so I researched the subject and wrote about it," says Gail Gibbons.

She began her research by visiting two newspapers, one in Vermont and one in New Hampshire. She said, "I watched people in the newsroom day after day, and I asked them a lot of questions. The one thing that really impressed me was that by the time they finished one newspaper, they were already working on the next one. There is one deadline after another. That's why I used the title."

line!

Newspaper

by Gail Gibbons

NEWSROOM

6:45 It is early morning. People all over the city are just waking up. But in the newsroom of *The News Gazette* the staff is already hard at work.

They have a deadline to meet . . . and it's only six hours away! By afternoon, today's edition of the newspaper will be printed and out to its readers. People will be able to read all the latest news.

The editor bursts through the door. He is the person in charge of the newspaper. "Production meeting in five minutes," he calls out.

dummy

7:06

At the meeting everyone is given a copy of the dummy for today's edition. The advertising department has already marked where all the ads will appear. Now the news writers can see how much space they will have for their articles.

A lot has happened in the world since yesterday's newspaper came out. The editor and his staff shuffle through piles of today's news items. They must decide which are the most important for them to write about.

There is world news, national news, local news. The group talks over all the possible stories. They look at photos, too.

"What about the water pipe break downtown?" someone says. "Our readers will want to know the facts." Everyone agrees. This will be the lead story.

Downtown, a reporter is at the scene, covering the story.

The production meeting goes on. Everyone has a different idea for today's headline. MAIN STREET FLOODED! That's it!

reporter

Back to the newsroom! World and national news stories keep coming in on the computers. They are beamed in by satellite. The newspaper pays for these "wire service" stories. This is another way for the staff to gather news.

8:05

ADVERTISING

8:20

Everyone writes and rewrites.

More news comes in. One of the city reporters calls in a story on a taxi drivers' strike.

The deadline is getting closer.

In the big newsroom, people work side by side at their different jobs.

The city editor is the person in charge of city news. He works with the reporter assigned to the water pipe break story.

Another reporter uses his portable computer to send in news about a barn fire. The information goes straight to the regional editor. He writes up the news of towns around the city.

city editor

DARKROOM
DON'T OPEN WHEN LIGHT IS ON!

photo editor

photographer

portable computer

regional editor

wire editor

photo receiver

Here comes a photographer. "I've got some great shots of the water pipe break!" he says. The darkroom crew takes his film to develop right away.

When the pictures are ready, the photo editor will pick the best ones.

At her desk, the wire editor rewrites a wire service story about the President's address to Congress. She waits for a wire service photo to come in over the receiver.

The sports editor is busy writing down the scores from all of last night's games.

The features editor prepares an article about a movie premiere. She checks her dummy to see how much space she has for fashions, food, and other features.

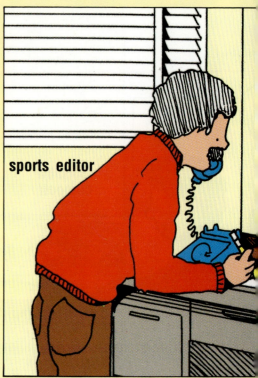

sports editor

editorial editor

Stacks and stacks of letters! The editorial editor is choosing which letters from readers will be in today's "Letters to the Editor" column.

He will also write the *Gazette's* editorial. Newspaper articles give facts about news events. Editorials give opinions about them.

features editor

artist

9:52

At her drawing board, a staff artist completes an illustration for an ad.

The wire editor has finished her national news
story. She begins to rewrite a foreign story.

The editor looks over the lead story about the
water pipe break. He makes sure everything has
been written correctly.

The deadline is less than three hours away.

COMPOSING ROOM

10:30

typesetting machine

The lead story is ready. The city editor uses his computer to send it to a typesetting machine in the composing room. Here, the story is set into type.

A pasteup artist has followed the dummy to make a layout for the front page. When he gets the type for the lead story, he cuts it out and pastes it into the layout. "This picture is too big," he says. "Take it to the camera room to be reduced."

pasteup artist

pasteup artist

layout

THE NEWS GAZETTE

MAIN STREET FLOODED!

11:06

Other parts of today's paper have already been pasted into the layouts. Ads are in position. So are the syndicated features that the newspaper buys—cartoons, columns, and articles that appear in the paper every day. Typeset news items can now be dropped into place.

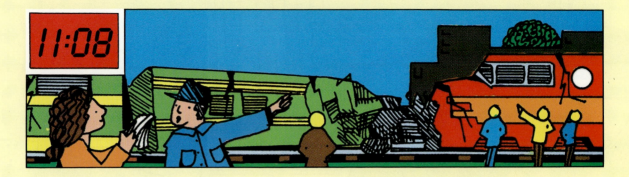

Wait! The front page layout must be changed! A very important story has just come in . . . there's been a big train crash. "Kill the water pipe story as the lead!" the editor says.

It's less than two hours to deadline!

A last-minute meeting is held. A reporter calls in with more facts. Luckily, no one was hurt in the wreck, but there is a lot of damage. A new story must be written quickly. The headline is changed . . . TRAINS COLLIDE! The old lead story is pushed back.

The composing room is even busier now. The train crash story is set into type. The new headline and story are cut and pasted into place. It looks like they'll make the deadline!

At the same time, editors come in to look over their sections. Ads are checked. This is the last chance to make sure everything is just right.

camera

printing plates

film

press supervisor

In the camera room most of the page layouts have been photographed already. "Here comes the front page," a camera operator says. The new layout is the last one to be photographed.

The films of the layouts are used to make printing plates.

The plates are put into place on the printing press.

"Start it up!" the supervisor shouts.

plate
(inside)

12:07

Huge rolls of paper, called newsprint, unwind from each unit of the press. The paper goes up . . . over . . . up . . . over . . .

The printing press makes a lot of noise!

The paper moves very fast. Both sides of the paper are printed at the same time.

ink rollers

blankets

plates

(to transfer ink from plates to paper)

The paper is gathered . . .
folded . . . cut . . . and . . .
out come finished newspapers!

Some of the newspapers are bundled and sent out immediately to stores and newsstands. Others will be delivered to homes or mailed to subscribers in many different towns and cities.

They made it! Today's newspaper is out on time.

And back in the *Gazette* newsroom everyone is at work getting ready for tomorrow's . . .

DEADLINE!

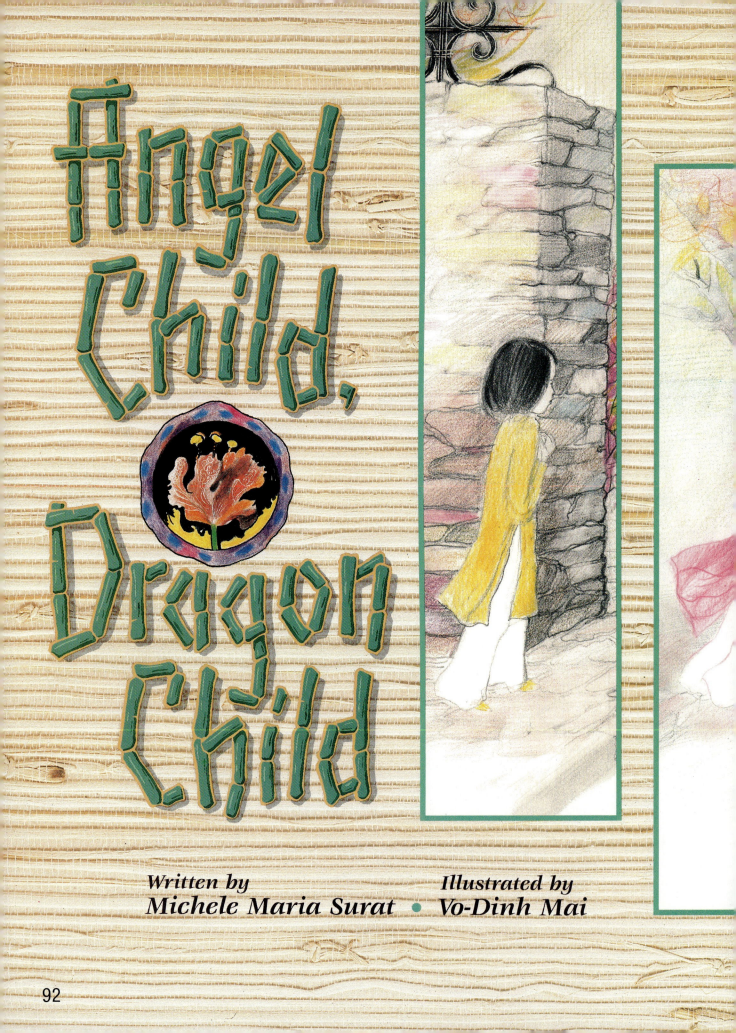

Angel Child, Dragon Child

Written by
Michele Maria Surat • Illustrated by
Vo-Dinh Mai

My sisters skipped through the stone gate
two by two. Mother was not there to skip with me.
Mother was far away in Vietnam. She could not say,
"Ut, my little one, be an Angel Child. Be happy in
your new American school."

I hugged the wall and peeked around the corner.

Ut (oot)

A boy with fire-colored hair pointed his finger. "Pajamas!" he shouted. "They wore white pajamas to school!" The American children tilted back their long noses, laughing.

I turned away. "I want to go home to Father and Little Quang," I said.

Chi Hai's hands curved over my shoulders. "Children stay where parents place them, Ut. We stay."

Little Quang (kwang)   Chi Hai (chee hi)

94

Somewhere, a loud bell jangled. I lost my sisters in a swirl of rushing children. "Pa-jaa-mas!" they teased.

Inside, the children did not sit together and chant as I was taught. Instead, they waved their hands and said their lessons one by one. I hid my hands, but the teacher called my name. "Nguyen Hoa."

Hoa is my true name, but I am Ut. Ut is my at-home name—a tender name for smallest daughter.

Nguyen Hoa (new-yen hwa)

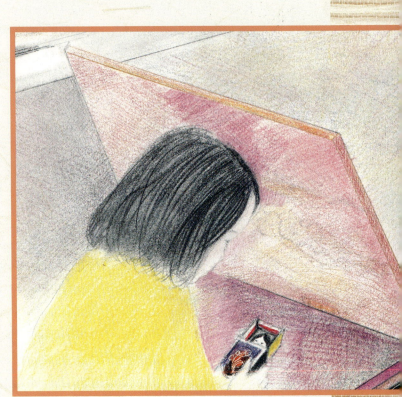

"**H**oa," the teacher said slowly. "Write your name, please." She pressed a chalk-piece to my hand and wrote in the air.

"I not understand," I whispered. The round-eyed children twittered. The red-haired boy poked my back.

"Stand up, Pajamas!"

I stood and bowed. *"Chao buoi sang,"* I said like an Angel Child. The children screeched like bluejays.

I sat down and flipped up my desk top, hiding my angry Dragon face.

chao buoi sang (chow bwee sung)

eep in my pocket, I felt Mother's gift—a small wooden matchbox with silvery edges. I took it out and traced the *hoa-phuong* on the lid. When I tapped the tiny drawer, Mother's eyes peeked over the edge.

"I will keep you safe in here, Mother," I told her. "See? You will just fit beside the crayons."

Her listening face smiled. In my heart, I heard the music of her voice. "Do not be angry, my smallest daughter," she said. "Be my brave little Dragon."

So all day I was brave, even when the children whispered behind their hands and the clock needles ticked slowly. Finally, the bell trilled. Time for home!

hoa-phuong (hwa fung)

As soon as he saw me, Little Quang crowed, "Ut! Ut! Ut!" His laughing eyes gleamed like watermelon seeds. I dropped my books and slung him on my hip.

There he rode, tugging my hair as I sorted mint leaves and chives. Little Quang strung rice noodles from the cup hooks. Father and I laughed at this happy play.

At night, small brother curled tight beside me. I showed him Mother's lonely face inside the matchbox. Together we prayed, "Keep Mother safe. Send her to us soon." With Mother's picture near, we slept like Angel Children.

In this way, many days passed.

One day at school, small feathers floated past the frosty windows. "Mother," I whispered, "this is snow. It makes everything soft, even the angry trees with no leaves to make them pretty."

My fingers danced on the desk top while I waited for the bell. When it rang, I rushed out the door.

Outside, snowflakes left wet kisses on my cheeks. "Chi Hai!" I called. "Catch some!"

"It disappears!" she cried.

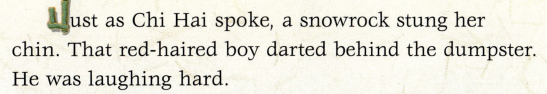

Just as Chi Hai spoke, a snowrock stung her chin. That red-haired boy darted behind the dumpster. He was laughing hard.

I tried, but I could not be a noble Dragon. Before I knew it, I was scooping up snow. My hands burned and my fingers turned red. I threw my snowrock and the laughing stopped.

Suddenly, the boy tackled me! We rolled in the snow, kicking and yelling, until the principal's large hand pinched my shoulder.

"Inside!" he thundered, and he marched us to our classroom.

"We can't have this fighting. You two have to help each other," ordered the principal. He pointed at me. "Hoa, you need to speak to Raymond. Use our words. Tell him about Vietnam." Raymond glared. "And you, Raymond, you must learn to listen. You will write Hoa's story."

"But I can't understand her funny words," Raymond whined. "Anyway, I don't have a pencil."

"Use this one, then," said the principal. He slapped down a pencil, turned and slammed the door. His shoes squeegeed down the hall.

"Pajamas!" Raymond hissed. He crinkled his paper and snapped the pencil in two. He hid his head in his arms. How could I tell my story to *him*?

The clock needles blurred before my eyes. No! I *would not* be an Angel Child for this cruel-hearted boy.

But later, across the room, I heard a sniffle. Raymond's shoulders jiggled like Little Quang's when he cried for Mother.

I crept over. Gently, I tugged the sad boy's sleeve. He didn't move. "Raymond," I pleaded, "not cry. I give you cookie."

Suddenly, his head bounced up. "Hoa!" he shouted. "You said my name. You didn't use funny words." He broke off a piece of the cookie.

"I say English," I answered proudly. "And you call me Ut. Ut is my at-home name, from Vietnam."

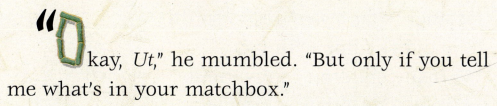

"Okay, *Ut*," he mumbled. "But only if you tell me what's in your matchbox."

"My mother," I told him. We giggled and ate the cookie crumbs.

Then Raymond asked, "Why do you need your mother's picture?"

"Mother is far away," I said softly.

"She didn't come with you?"

"So many children in my family," I sighed. "No money for Mother to come."

"Wait," said Raymond. He grabbed part of the broken pencil. I handed him a new sheet of paper. "Now tell me about Vietnam," he said.

Raymond scrawled my words in black squiggles. I crayoned pictures in the margins.

When we were ready, Raymond leaned out the door. "Done!" he beamed. He waved the story like a flag.

The principal squeegeed up the hall. "You may go," said the big man.

We dashed through the stone gate together.

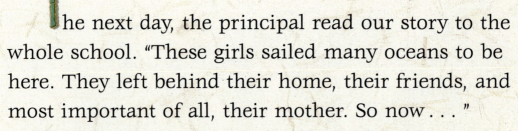

The next day, the principal read our story to the whole school. "These girls sailed many oceans to be here. They left behind their home, their friends, and most important of all, their mother. So now . . . "

"Ut's mother needs money for the long boat ride to America!" shouted a familiar voice. Raymond stood on his chair. "And we could have a fair and *earn* the money."

"Young man!" warned the principal.

Raymond slid down in his seat. "We could," he insisted. I hid my eyes. I held my breath. Chi Hai squeezed my hand.

"A special fair! A Vietnamese fair!" my teacher exclaimed. My eyes opened wide.

The principal's eyebrows wiggled like caterpillars. "But who will help with a Vietnamese fair?"

"Me!" cried Raymond.

"We will!" squealed the children.

"Well, what are we waiting for?" said the principal. And we all clapped for the fair.

On the special day, I wore my white *ao dai* and welcomed everyone to our Vietnamese fair. "*Chao buoi sang,*" I said, bowing like an Angel Child. "*Chao buoi sang,*" they answered, smiling.

ao dai (ow zi)

High above our heads, our rainbow dragon floated freely. Below, Chi Hai and her friends sold rice cakes, imperial rolls and sesame cookies. Raymond popped balloons and won three goldfish. He gave one to Little Quang. "Don't eat it," he warned.

By the end of the day, we had just enough money to send to Mother. "When will she come?" I wondered.

very day, we walked home wondering, "When will Mother come?"

We slid through icy winter. . . .

We splish-splashed through spring rain. . . .

We tiptoed barefoot through the grass, still hoping she would come.

On the last day of school, when I knew the *hoa-phuong* were blossoming in Vietnam, Raymond and I raced home faster than all my sisters. We were the first to see Father and Little Quang at the picture window, and beside them . . .

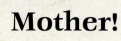

Mother!

Meet Michele Maria Surat and Vo-Dinh Mai

Michele Maria Surat explains that *Angel Child, Dragon Child* is a make-believe story, but she got the idea from having Vietnamese students in her classes. She says, "I was impressed by my Vietnamese students who had the courage to create new lives in America, so I wanted to write about them."

Ms. Surat knows how hard it is to go to a new school. She adds, "Between the ages of nine and sixteen I went to a different school every year. My mother is Puerto Rican. My father is Czechoslovakian. I grew up with parents from two different cultures. Each culture has its own stories to tell in its own language."

Vo-Dinh Mai was born in Vietnam but has lived in France and in the United States. He says, "There is a very definite message in *Angel Child, Dragon Child*: People of every country and race have the same concerns, the same problems, and the same hopes and dreams.

"Each country's history and culture is different, but human beings are basically the same no matter where they live."

Vo-Dinh Mai is also the illustrator of another children's book, *First Snow*.

IT'S DARK IN HERE

I am writing these poems
From inside a lion,
And it's rather dark in here.
So please excuse the handwriting
Which may not be too clear.
But this afternoon by the lion's cage
I'm afraid I got too near.
And I'm writing these lines
From inside a lion,
And it's rather dark in here.

SHEL SILVERSTEIN

117

CONTENTS

Make new friends
but keep the old;
One is silver and the
other gold.

TRADITIONAL SONG

WELCOME TO THE

MEET
ELIZABETH WINTHROP

Elizabeth Winthrop wrote *The Best Friends Club* because of what happened to her as a child. She says, "I grew up with five brothers. Like Lizzie, I always made rules, but they paid no attention to me."

Ms. Winthrop thinks friendship is important to all children. She adds, "My children were always worried about having friends. How do I get a best friend? Will I keep her or him? What's a best friend like?"

She says about her writing, "When I write, I go into myself and find out what I'm feeling."

She adds, "I love writing for children. *The Best Friends Club* is a sequel to *Lizzie and Harold*. I knew their story wasn't over, so I wrote another one."

MEET MARTHA WESTON

Martha Weston was very excited about illustrating *The Best Friends Club* because she likes Lizzie so much.

She explains, "As a child, I was really bossy and had to show everyone how to do everything. Everything had to be done the way I wanted it to be done. Lizzie is like that, and I love her because she reminds me of myself.

"When I began drawing Lizzie and Harold, I asked my daughter and her friend to model for me. I asked them to do the things that Lizzie and Harold do in the story, and I took pictures of them. I paid them ten cents each for every picture I took."

THE BEST FRIENDS CLUB

BY ELIZABETH WINTHROP

ILLUSTRATED BY MARTHA WESTON

Lizzie and Harold were best friends.
Harold taught Lizzie how to do cat's cradle.
Lizzie taught Harold how to play running bases.

Lizzie shared her trick-or-treat candy with Harold, and Harold let Lizzie ride his big red bike.

They always walked home from school together.

"Let's start a best friends club," Lizzie said one day.

"Great," said Harold. "We can meet under your porch. That will be our clubhouse."

Harold painted the sign.

It said

THE BF CLUB.

"Now write *Members Only,*" said Lizzie.

"You write it," said Harold. "My teacher says my M's are too fat."

So Lizzie wrote *Members Only.*

"Who are the members?" Harold asked.

"You and me," said Lizzie.

"That's all?"

"Yes," said Lizzie. "You can be the president and I'll be the vice-president. The president gets to write down all the rules."

"You be the president," Harold said. "Your writing is better than mine."

"All right, then I'll be president," said Lizzie. "Now we'll make up the rules."

"Rule number one," said Harold. "The club meets under Lizzie's porch."

"Right," said Lizzie. "Rule number two. Nobody else can be in the club."

"Rule number three," said Harold. He thought for a long time. "I can't think of any more."

"Rule number three," said Lizzie. "Lizzie and Harold walk home from school together every day."

"Rule number four," said Harold. "Everybody in the club knows cat's cradle."

They heard voices. Someone was walking by. They could see two pairs of feet.

"It's Christina," whispered Lizzie. "She always wears those black party shoes."

"And Douglas," Harold whispered back. "His shoelaces are always untied."

"I'm only having Nancy and Amy and Stacey to my birthday party," they heard Christina say.

"My mother said I could have my whole class," Douglas answered. "We're going to play baseball."

"Oh goody," said Harold. "That means I'll be invited to Douglas's birthday party."

"I won't," Lizzie said gloomily. She was in a different class.

The next day, Harold came out of his classroom with Douglas.

"He wants to walk home with us," Harold said to Lizzie.

"He can't," said Lizzie.

"Why not?" asked Harold.

"Harold, remember the rules. We're best friends and we always walk home together," Lizzie said. "Just you and me."

"Oh yeah," said Harold. "I forgot."

Douglas looked very sad.

"Sorry, Douglas," Harold said. "See you tomorrow."

"Douglas's ears stick out," Lizzie said on the way home.

"So what?" said Harold.

"His shoelaces are always dripping," said Lizzie.

"I don't care about that," said Harold.

"I'll meet you in the clubhouse after snacks," said Lizzie.

"I can't come today," said Harold. "My mother wants me home."

Lizzie sat in the clubhouse all by herself.
She wrote down more rules.
They said

5. Best friends don't go to other people's birthday parties.

6. People with funny ears and drippy shoelaces are not allowed in the club.

The next day, Harold came out of his classroom with Douglas again.

"Douglas asked me to play at his house," said Harold.

"*Harold*," said Lizzie. "What about the club?"

"What club?" asked Douglas.

"None of your business," said Lizzie.

"I'll come tomorrow," said Harold. "I promise."

Lizzie watched them walk away together. She stuck out her tongue at them but Harold didn't turn around.

She went straight to the clubhouse and wrote down another rule. It said

7. Best friends don't go to other people's houses to play.

Then she threw a ball at the garage wall until suppertime.

"Douglas wants to be in the club," said Harold the next day.

"He can't be," said Lizzie. "Only best friends are allowed in this club."

She showed him all the new rules she had written down.

"This club is no fun," said Harold. "It has too many rules. I quit."

He crawled out from under the porch and walked home.

Lizzie took down his sign and put up a new one.

Douglas came down the street.

He was riding Harold's new bicycle.

Harold was chasing after him.

When Harold saw the sign, he stopped and read it.

"What does it say?" asked Douglas.

"It says, 'Lizzie's Club. Nobody Else Allowed,'"
Harold said.

Harold leaned over and looked at Lizzie. "You can't
have a club with only one person," he said.

"*I* can," said Lizzie.

"A three-person club is more fun," said Harold.
"Douglas knows how to do cat's cradle."
"But he's not a best friend,"
said Lizzie.

"It'll be a different kind of club," said Harold.
"We'll make up a new name."

"Maybe," said Lizzie.

She sat under the porch and watched them.

First they played bicycle tag.

Then they threw the ball at her garage wall.

"**W**ant to play running bases?" Lizzie asked.

"I don't know how," said Douglas.

"I'll teach you," said Lizzie.

They took turns being the runner. Lizzie was the fastest.

Douglas whispered something to Harold.

"Douglas wants you to come to his birthday party," said Harold.

Then Lizzie whispered something to Harold.

"Lizzie says yes," Harold said to Douglas.

"And I've thought of a new name for the club," said Lizzie. "Douglas can be in it too."

"Oh boy!" said Douglas.

"You can be the first member. I am the president and Harold is the vice-president," said Lizzie.

"That's okay with me," said Harold.

"Me too," said Douglas.

It was getting dark.

Douglas went home for supper.

Lizzie crawled back under the porch. She tore up her sign and her list of rules.

"What's the new name for the club?" Harold asked.

"I'll show you," said Lizzie.

She sat down and wrote in great big letters
THE NO RULES CLUB.

Harold smiled.

He stuck up the sign with a thumbtack.

Then they both went upstairs to Lizzie's house
for supper.

GREETING

Hujambo rafiki yangu!
(Swahili)

Konnichiwa,
watashi no tomo!
(Japanese)

Hello, my friend!
(English)

140

EACH OTHER

ZDRAVSTVUI MOI DRUG! (RUSSIAN)

Bonjour, mon ami! (French)

¡HOLA MI AMIGO! (SPANISH)

Laura's new this year in school.

She acts so opposite, it seems like a rule.

If someone says yes, Laura says no.

If someone says high, Laura says low.

If you say bottom, she'll say top.

If you say go, she'll always stop.

If you say short, Laura says tall.

If you say none, she says all.

If you say beginning, Laura says end...

But today she asked me to be her friend.

I said maybe

But not quite yes.

Then I said, "Want to take a walk?"

And Laura said, "I guess."

Jeff Moss

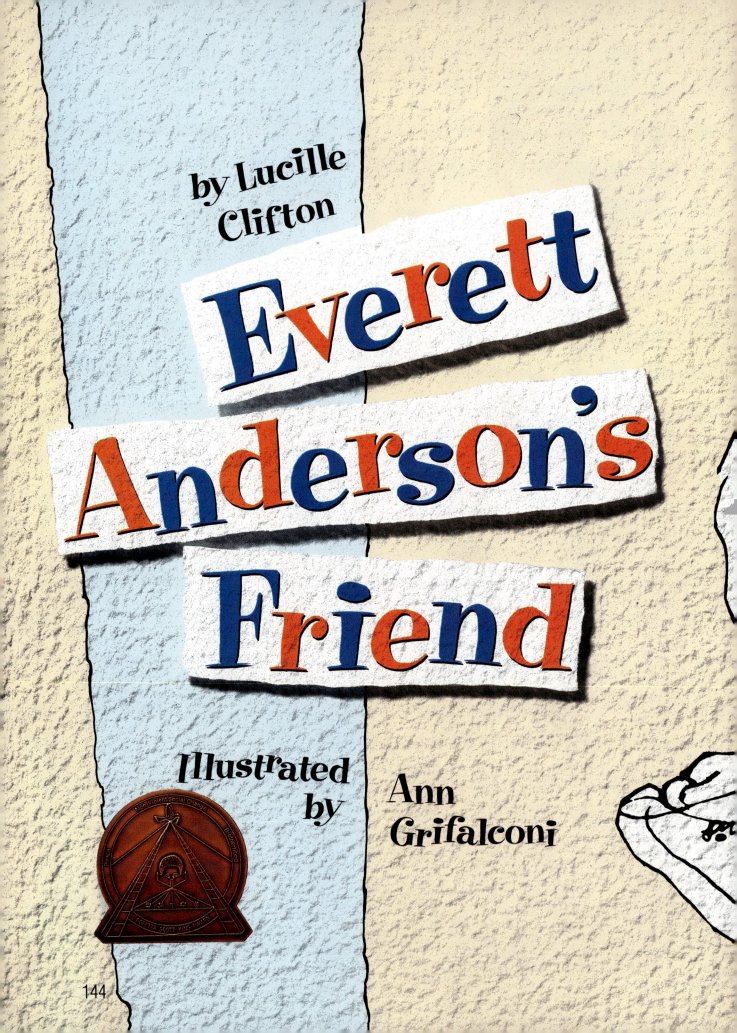

by Lucille
Clifton

Everett Anderson's Friend

Illustrated
by

Ann
Grifalconi

Someone new has come to stay
in 13A, in 13A
and Everett Anderson's Mama and he
can't wait to see, can't wait to see
whether it's girls or
whether it's boys and
how are their books and
how are their toys and
where they've been and
where they go and
who are their friends and
the people they know,
oh, someone new has come to stay
next door in 13A.

If not an almost
brother,
why not something
other
like a bird or
a cat or
a cousin or
a dozen uncles?

Please,
says Everett Anderson softly,
why did they have to be
a family of
shes?

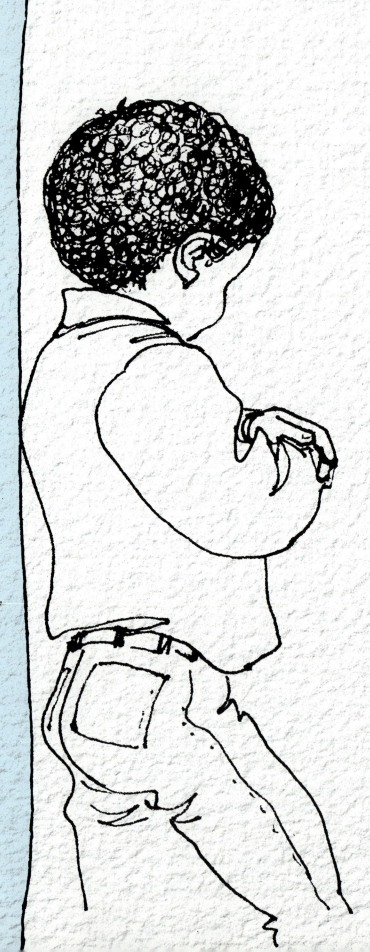

Girls named Maria who
win at ball
are not a bit of fun
at all.
No, girls who can run
are just no fun
thinks Everett Anderson!

In 14A when Mama's at work
sometimes Joe and sometimes Kirk
can come till she gets home and be
Everett Anderson's company.

Three boys are just the right amount
for playing games that count,
there isn't any room, you see,
for girls named Maria in company.

If Daddy was here
he would let me in and
call me a careless boy
and then
(even though I
 forgot my key)
he would make peanut butter
and jelly for me,
and not be mad
and I'd be glad.

If Daddy was here
he could let me in
thinks Everett Anderson
again.

A girl named Maria
is good to know
when you haven't got
any place to go
and you forgot your
apartment key.

Why, she can say,
"Come in with me,
and play in 13A and wait
if your Mama is working late."

Even if she beats at races it's
nicer to lose in familiar places.

Maria's Mama makes little pies
called *Tacos,*
calls little boys *Muchachos,*
and likes to thank the *Dios;*
oh, 13A is a lovely surprise
to Everett Anderson's eyes!

A girl named Maria
who wins at ball
is fun to play with
after all
and Joe and Kirk and
Maria too
are just the right number
for things to do.

Lose a key,
win a friend,
things have a way of
balancing out,
Everett Anderson's Mama explains,
and that's what the world is all about.

And the friends we find
are full of surprises
Everett Anderson realizes.

Meet Lucille Clifton

"*Everett Anderson's Friend* is about giving new and different people a chance," says Lucille Clifton. "You might not like some people because they seem different. I've found if you reach across differences and get to know people, you will find they have things to teach you."

When asked if Everett Anderson is a real person, she says, "He's not. I just wanted to write a book about a boy who was poor in things but not in spirit."

Ms. Clifton adds, "I learned about Everett Anderson by paying attention to children around me. The story is set in a housing project in a big city. I wrote the story in rhyme, because I care about the sound of music in language."

Talking to children about her books is something Ms. Clifton enjoys doing. She says that children often tell her that they are like Everett Anderson. They say, "I know just how he feels. I feel that way, too."

Meet Ann Grifalconi

When Ann Grifalconi drew the pictures for *Everett Anderson's Friend,* she pretended to be all the people—the mother, the grandmother, Everett, the girl. She says, "I tried to get inside that person's eyes and see how that person looks at another person. Then I acted the story out and felt it inside so I could draw it."

As a child, Ann Grifalconi moved a lot. She knows what it's like to move from place to place. She says, "I was always terrified to go to a new place. I understood how the girl in *Everett Anderson's Friend* felt.

"When I moved, I tried to get to know my neighbors. Soon I found I could move and make new friends. I found I could make changes, and I could be happy."

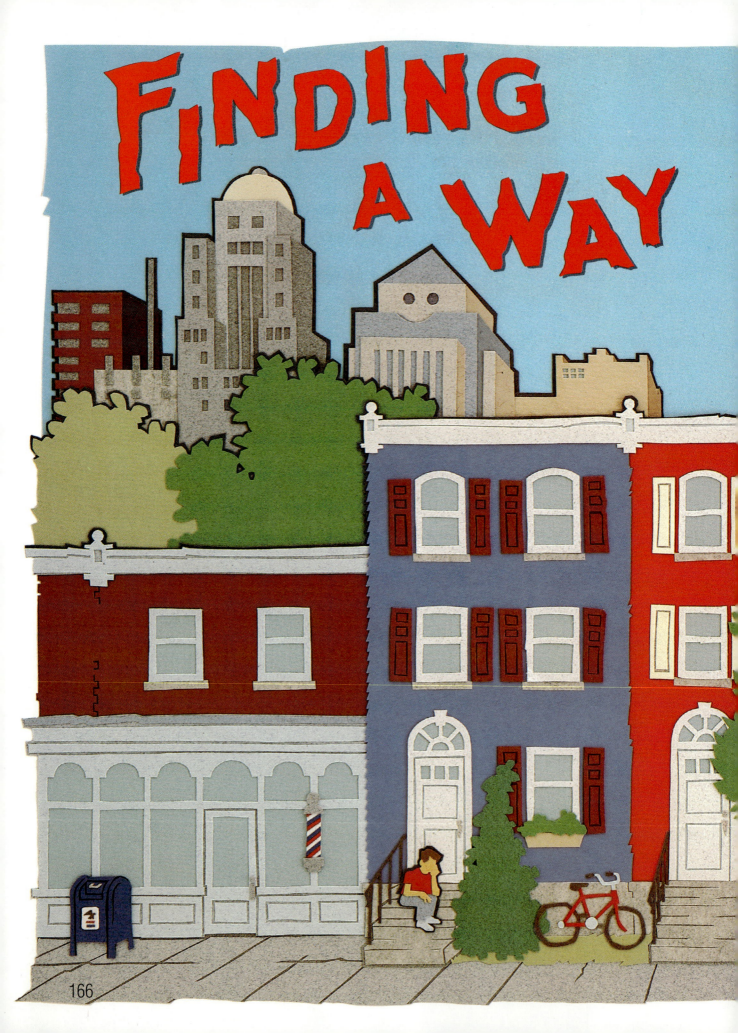

FINDING A WAY

I'd like you for a friend.
I'd like to find the way
Of asking you to be my friend.
I don't know what to say.

What would you like to hear?
What is it I can do?
There has to be some word, some look
Connecting me to you.

MYRA COHN LIVINGSTON

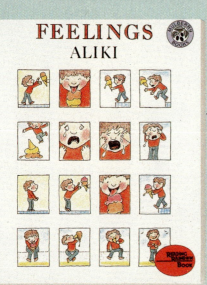

Feelings
Written and illustrated by Aliki
Mulberry Books, 1986

Two and Too Much
by Mildred Pitts Walter
illustrated by Pat Cummings
Bradbury Press, 1990

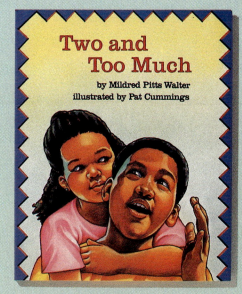

GETTING TO KNOW YOU

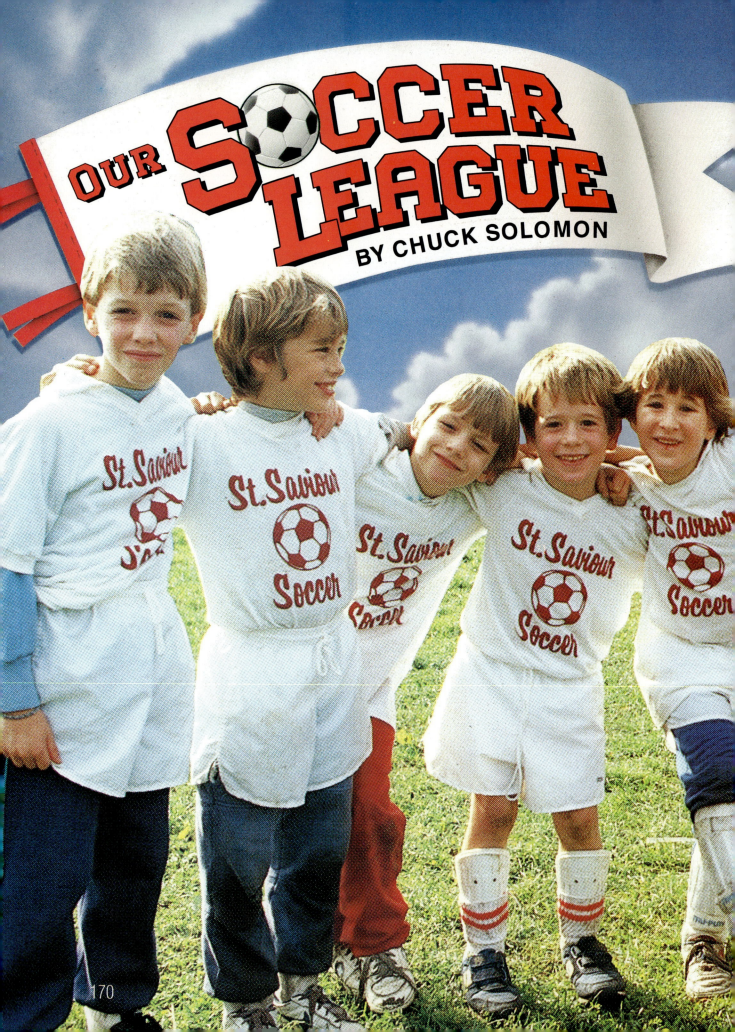

OUR SOCCER LEAGUE

BY CHUCK SOLOMON

WE'RE THE FALCONS. WE PLAY SOCCER!

Today the game is with our friends, the Sluggers. They wear blue shirts.

First everyone stretches.

Then we practice.

In soccer, you dribble the ball with your feet.

You pass to your teammates.

And you try to kick the ball through the goal, if you can.

Goalies need practice, too. They stop the other team from scoring, and they're the only players on the field who can touch the ball with their hands.

Falcons' goal

Falcons (white shirts)

Out-of-bounds

Sluggers (blue shirts)

Sluggers' goal

It's game time!

The coaches give us our positions for the opening kickoff.

The Sluggers kick off and burst downfield. They charge to the goal. There's a goal kick.

Defense! Our goalie, Toby, makes a save. Toby throws it out, and we have the ball.

Eric dribbles to midfield . . . with the Sluggers in pursuit. Eric passes . . .

but a Slugger intercepts! He gets his foot behind the ball . . . and boots it!

The Sluggers have the ball.

But then it is kicked out-of-bounds. Whenever a team puts the ball out, the other team throws it back in.

Moira throws it in for us.

"Don't use your hands, Johnny!"

Eric booms it.

Score! It's one to nothing, Falcons.

Teams	1st half	2nd half	Final
Falcons	1		
Sluggers			

But not for long.

The Sluggers bounce right back and tie the game.

It's now one to one.

Teams	1st half	2nd half	Final
Falcons	1		
Sluggers	1		

The score is still tied at one to one when the coaches call halftime.

Whew! It feels good to take a break.

After a ten-minute rest . . .

we're back to the game!

We charge down to the Slugger's goal.

Olivier's kick is wide . . .

and the Sluggers take the ball.

Here comes our defense
at midfield.
    The two players collide.

    It's anybody's ball.

    The Sluggers and Falcons
battle for the ball.

    The ball goes up . . .

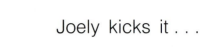

Joely kicks it . . .

Oh, no! "Hand ball!" Since a Slugger touched the ball, we get a free kick.

Jonathan booms it and we have control again.

No one scored, and the clock is running out. Only five minutes are left in the game.

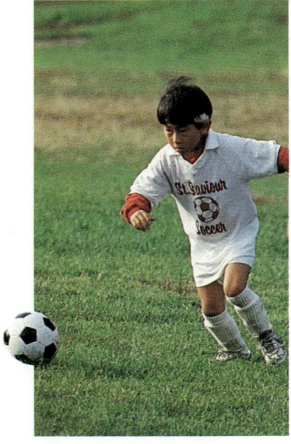

5:00

3:00

2:00 Out-of-bounds on a header.

Ted throws it in.

The Sluggers boot the ball
into the open field.

1:00

John's set . . . boom!

Score! It's two to one, Sluggers!

We try our best to tie
the score . . .

but the clock runs out.

0:00

Teams	1st half	2nd half	Final
Falcons	1	0	1
Sluggers	1	1	2

The Sluggers celebrate . . .

and we give ourselves a cheer.

When you play a great game . . .

everybody wins!

MEET CHUCK SOLOMON

"I wanted to write *Our Soccer League* because soccer is such a good sport for children," says Chuck Solomon. "Soccer doesn't require much equipment, it's not too rough, and running is good exercise. Besides, both girls and boys can play it together."

Mr. Solomon wrote this book to show children how to play soccer. He said, "I also wanted to show the excitement and feelings you get when you play the game.

"I photographed this book during an actual game, just as it happens in the book. As I was taking pictures, an editor was writing what was happening. After I developed the photographs, I wrote the story. It was important for me to tell the story just the way it happened."

BY **K**ATHLEEN M. MULDOON
Illustrated by Linda Shute

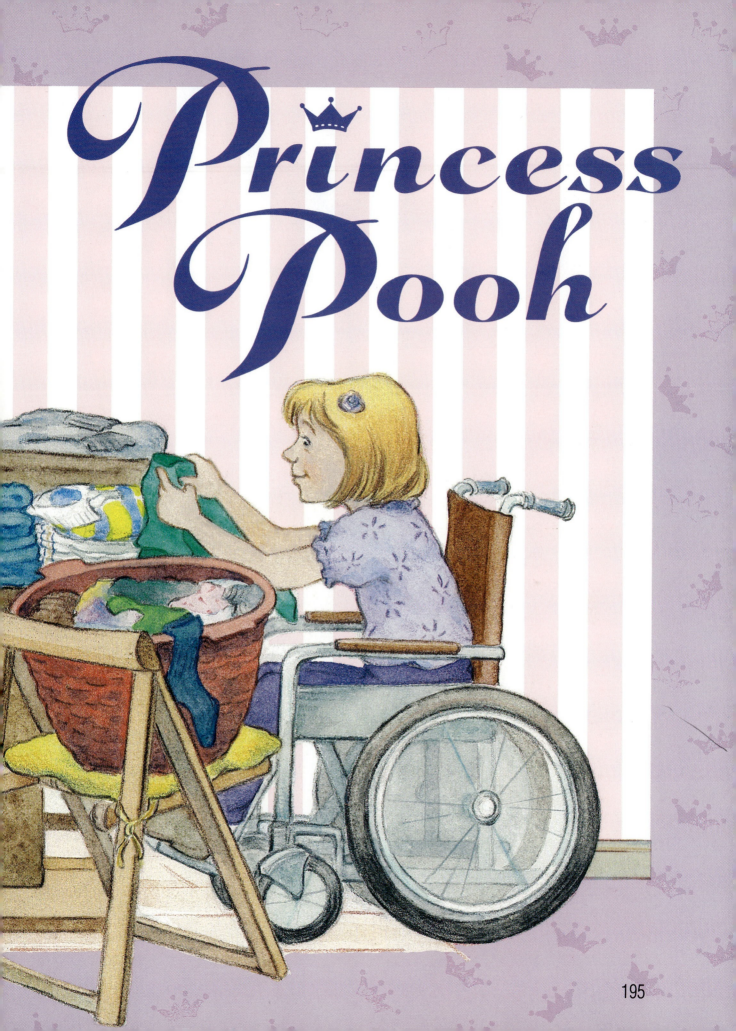

Princess Pooh

My big sister is ten years old. Her name is Penelope Marie Piper, but everyone calls her Penny. Everyone except me. I, Patty Jean Piper, call her Princess Pooh. No one knows I call her that, but it's the perfect name for her. All day she just sits on her throne with wheels and tells everybody in the whole world what to do.

Mrs. Meadows COOKIES

When we go shopping at the mall, Princess Pooh rides on her throne while Dad wheels her around. She smiles and waves like she's some kind of movie star. Mom carries the Princess's crutches and I, Patty Jean the Servant, carry packages. Sometimes there are so many I look like a box with legs.

Everyone loves the Princess. Grandma and Grandpop and all the aunts and uncles and cousins in our family hug her and say how sweet and wonderful she is. Then they look at me and say I am growing like a weed. That's the way it has been for a million years. The Princess is a flower. I, plain old Patty Jean, am a weed.

Once we went to a carnival. Princess Pooh watched me ride a hundred times on the roller coaster. It was fun, but it would have been better with a friend. I almost wished the Princess could ride with me. Then I tried to win a pink stuffed poodle. I spent all my allowance and threw a thousand balls, but I couldn't knock down the bottles. When we left, the man handed Princess Pooh a yellow stuffed poodle with a diamond collar! That's how it is. Everyone gives her things.

My school is a hundred years old. It is so far from my house I have to ride for hours on a school bus to get there. Princess Pooh goes to the new school right across the street. She can wheel herself there in one second.

If it rains, Dad carries her and her throne to his car and gives her a one-second ride. I, Patty Jean, wear an icky yellow raincoat and stand in mud puddles, waiting for the bus.

Saturday is chore day. Mom mows the lawn. Dad washes clothes and cleans the garage. Then he brings the clean clothes to the Princess, and she folds them into piles on the table. I, Patty Jean the Maid, clean the bathroom.

One Saturday, Mom asked me to fold clothes because Princess Pooh had therapy. I sat at the table pretending I was the Princess. I folded the clothes very fast and put them in perfect stacks. When the Princess came home, I waited for Mom to tell her to clean the bathroom. But Mom put her right to bed because she was tired. So I, exhausted Patty Jean, had to clean the bathroom, too.

It is summer now. All my friends have gone to camp—everyone except me. Mom says there's no money to send me to camp because the Princess got new braces for her legs.

Princess Pooh doesn't need them anyway because all she does is sit. She only takes little tiny walks, like when she has to go to the bathroom at a restaurant and her wheelchair won't fit through the door. Mom says she walks at therapy, too, but I've never seen her do it.

After dinner I go outside. The Princess is in the hammock reading a book.

"Do you want to make a puppet show?" I ask.

"No, thanks," she says in her princess voice. "I'm going to read lots of books so I can win a prize in the summer reading program."

I don't feel like reading, but I get a book anyway and look at the pictures. I am finished in one minute.

"This book is boring," I say. "Let's play with puppets now." The Princess doesn't answer. I look over at the hammock—there she is, asleep.

Behind the tree is the throne. Seeing it empty gives me the best idea anyone in the whole world has ever had. Today I, Patty Jean, will be the Princess!

I sit on the throne. It is covered with cushions and feels like a cloud.

"I will rest on my golden throne for the whole evening," I say. I imagine all the people in my kingdom, looking at me and loving their beautiful new princess.

The throne is hard to wheel on the grass, so I get up and pull it to the front yard. "Now I will spend *every minute* on the throne," I say.

I decide to ride to the Princess's school. There is a nice, steep little hill on the grass near the sidewalk. Maybe it would be fun to ride down it. I sit down and give the throne a good, hard push.

PLOP! The throne dumps me out on the sidewalk and lands upside down on top of me. My knee has a tiny cut on it, but it doesn't hurt much. Still, I'm glad no one is around to laugh. I wonder if Princess Pooh ever fell when she was learning. I put the throne rightside up and get back on it. Then I ride to the corner. I go down the low place on the curb so I can cross the street.

When the light turns green, I push the wheels as fast as I can. I make it to the island in the middle, but then the light turns red again.

Cars and trucks and buses rush by. I cover my face so I will not see myself go SPLAT.

Finally, the traffic stops and the light is green again. I finish crossing the street. I push the throne up the low place at the crosswalk. It is hard to go uphill, but I do it. I wheel down the sidewalk. I've been pushing so hard I feel like both my arms are broken.

Some grown-ups are walking toward me. They look at me and my throne, and then they turn away fast, like I do when I'm watching a scary movie. Does this happen to Princess Pooh?

Some boys are playing on the sidewalk and will not move out of my way. "Why don't you go over me, Wheel Legs?" says one of them. All his friends laugh. "I'll beat you up!" I yell, but they just laugh some more and run away.

I see an ice-cream truck on the school playground. Lots of big kids are crowded around it. I make a shortcut across the baseball field, but by the time I get there and take some money out of my pocket, the worst thing in the world has happened. Great big raindrops have started falling over everything! SLAM goes the window on the truck. The children squeal and run away.

The man drives off and I'm alone on my wet throne.

The rain comes faster and faster. I think about running home, too, but I can't leave the throne out in the rain. Besides, I am still the Princess. I'm spending every minute on my throne, even if I do get wet! So I push harder and harder. When I get back to the baseball field, I can see it's a muddy mess. The wheels of the throne sink down, down, down. They stop turning. My hands are covered with mud. I jump off the throne, and my new sandals sink, too. My feet go with them. By the time I pull the throne out, I am wetter and colder than I have ever been in my whole life. I, Princess Patty Jean, am a royal mess. It is definitely time to quit sitting on the throne.

The rain stops. Across the street there is a rainbow. I notice Dad standing in our front yard. He is calling and calling, but the cars and trucks are so noisy I can't hear him. Mom is walking up the street, looking around. I drag the muddy throne across the rest of the field to the sidewalk.

Then I cross the street. When Mom sees me, she runs and holds out her arms. Dad is right behind her. "I didn't mean to mess up the throne. I'm sorry," I say.

"Throne?" says Mom. "Oh, the *wheelchair*. We thought you were lost!"

"You weren't looking for the chair?" I say.

"Patty Jean, we were looking for *you*." Mom hugs me some more. "You shouldn't have taken Penny's chair. But we're so glad you're back!"

Since Hanna Moved Away

The tires on my bike are flat.
The sky is grouchy gray.
At least it sure feels like that
Since Hanna moved away.

Chocolate ice cream tastes like prunes.
December's come to stay.
They've taken back the Mays and Junes
Since Hanna moved away.

Flowers smell like halibut.
Velvet feels like hay.
Every handsome dog's a mutt
Since Hanna moved away.

Nothing's fun to laugh about.
Nothing's fun to play.
They call me, but I won't come out
Since Hanna moved away.

JUDITH VIORST

CONTENTS

UNIT 3

Water, Water Everywhere

Inviting, rippling waters
Waiting for little toes
Hurry, go get changed!

MARGARET BENDIG
Age 10, United States

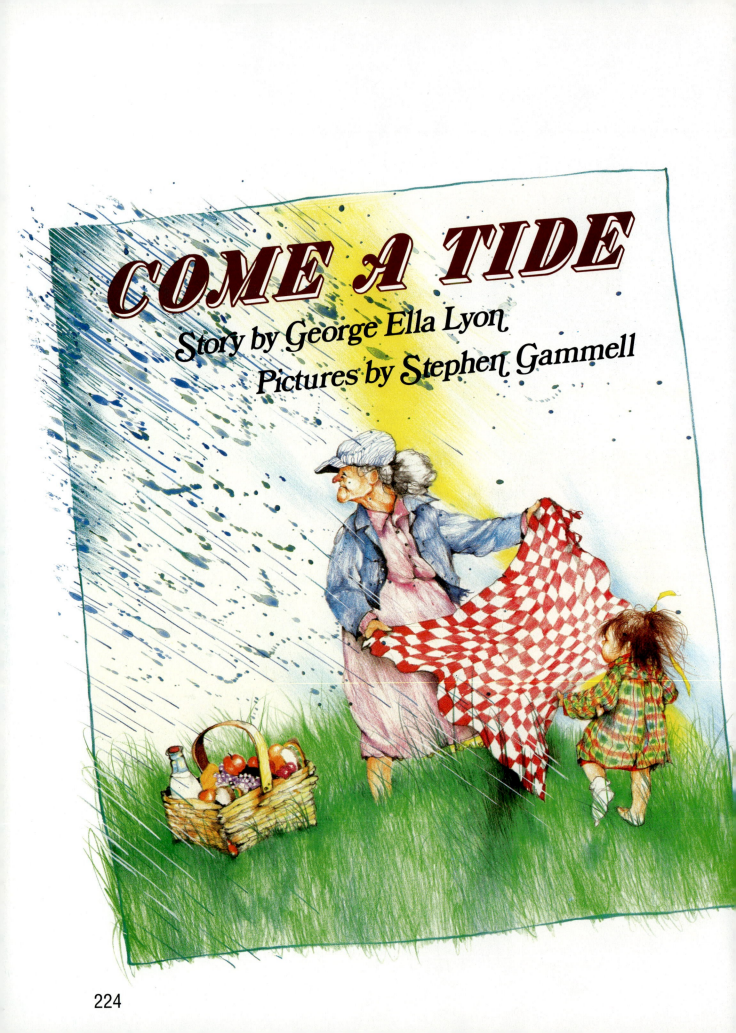

COME A TIDE

Story by George Ella Lyon

Pictures by Stephen Gammell

Last March it snowed
and then it rained
for four days and nights.

"It'll come a tide,"
my grandma said.

And sure enough,
when all the creeks
rushed down to the river
like kinfolks coming home,

it did.

It washed away
little naked gardens
on Clover Fork

pigs and chickens
on Martins Fork

and a whole front porch
on Poor Fork.

We stood on our bridge
and watched them swirl by.
Ooo-eee! Ooo-eee! cried the pigs.
The river nudged the bridge bottom.

Still we boasted,
"It won't flood us."

But we left our radios crackling
that night when we went to sleep.

The warning whistle
didn't have to blow twice.

Cloudburst! the radio said.
Wall of water coming down!

In five minutes
we'd jumped in our clothes
and were outside headed for the truck.

"Did you hear the whistle?
Do you want to go with us?"
Mama called to our
neighbor, Mrs. Mac.

"Joe won't go
till he finds his teeth
so I've put a pot of coffee on."

"Did you hear the whistle?
Do you want to go with us?"
Mama called to the Cains across the street.

"I can't catch Donald!" John yelled back.

"It's that duck," his mother hollered.
"John has to save the one thing that swims.
Don't stall on our account."

"Did you hear the whistle?
Do you want to go with us?"
Mama called to Papa Bill next door.

"I heard it, honey.
But I've got me a boat
and I'm aiming to find the oars."

Rain came down like curtains
as we drove up Grandma's hill.

239

She fed us warmed-over biscuits
and coffee stout as a post.
Then she sent us to bed.

When light flooded in
and I was asleep,
Daddy went out scouting.

And we did.

The Macs, the Cains, Papa Bill:
next day everyone was shoveling.
Soggy furniture and mud-mapped rugs
made mountains in front of each house.

"It got us this time,"
we had to admit, taking
lunch at the rescue wagon.

But we dug and hauled,
we scrubbed and crawled
to find our buried treasure.

Now we'll be fine,
except in spring
when the snow and rain
come together.

Then I'll hold my breath
and hope Grandma won't say,
"Children, it'll come a tide."

Meet
GEORGE ELLA LYON

George Ella Lyon was born and raised in Harlan, Kentucky, in the rural hills of the Appalachian Mountains. *Come a Tide* was based on the real events and people where she grew up.

In 1977, there really was water "up to the piano keys" of her parents' house. Ms. Lyon says that all the neighbors in the story are real—John really tried to catch his duck, Donald; Papa Bill was looking for the oars to his boat; and Joe wouldn't go until he found his teeth.

"The hard part of writing the story," she said, "was trying to figure out what to leave out.

"As I began writing, I was flooded with memories. I wrote down everything, and then searched for the events that made a story.

"Books come out of people's lives, and you write about what you know," Ms. Lyon said. "We breathe in experience and breathe out stories."

Meet
STEPHEN GAMMELL

Hello everybody,

So often floods are terrible. Belongings are lost or damaged, homes are wrecked, and animals are swept away. Saddest of all is when someone drowns. But *Come a Tide* is about people and animals getting by in spite of the flood. They're even having fun!

You see that the pigs are especially having fun. And when all those folks stand on the bridge and look up at the rain, do you think they care about getting wet? Not a bit. That's just part of the fun. It's a nice evening for Papa Bill to take the dog for a boat ride. And a fine time to go visit Grandma! They are making the best of it. Do you do that?

I drew the pictures with regular old colored pencils on smooth heavy paper. All the rain, the splashes, and splotches I did with watercolor. I wanted some of the pages to look wet—like this book was left out in the rain. What do you think?

Your friend,

Stephen Gammell

APRIL RAIN SONG

Let the rain kiss you.
Let the rain beat upon your head with silver liquid drops.
Let the rain sing you a lullaby.

The rain makes still pools on the sidewalk.
The rain makes running pools in the gutter.
The rain plays a little sleep-song on our roof at night—

And I love the rain.

Langston Hughes

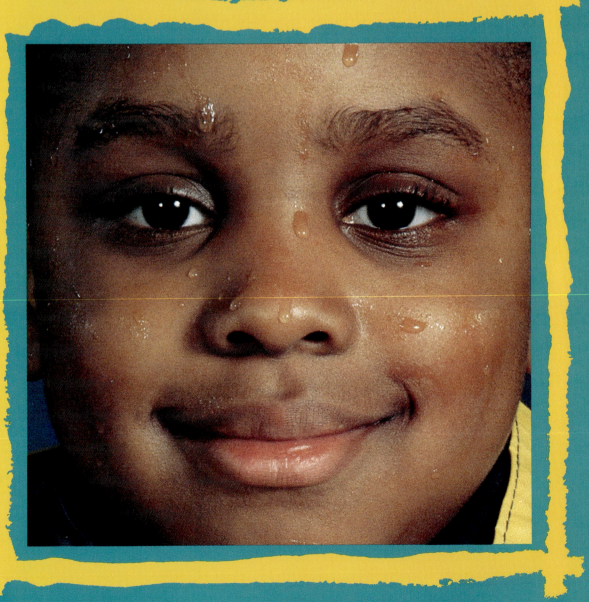

COLORES DE CARACOL

Colores de caracol
arco iris en el cielo
es la bandera del sol.

The rainbow showing
through the rain
says the sun
will shine again.

Ernesto Galarza

The Sun, the Wind

The Sun, the Wind and the Rain

Lisa Westberg Peters · Illustrated by Ted Rand

by Lisa Westberg Peters
Illustrated by Ted Rand

and the Rain

This is the story of two mountains. The earth made one. Elizabeth in her yellow sun hat made the other.

The earth made its mountain millions of years ago.
It began as a pool underground, first fiery hot and soft,
then cold and rock-hard.

Elizabeth made hers on the beach today with bucketsful of wet sand.

Eons passed. The earth cracked and shifted until
the rock of its mountain slowly rose.

Elizabeth quickly piled her sand high. She patted it
smooth all the way around.

The earth mountain sparkled against the sky.
Furry animals walked in its lush green valleys.

Elizabeth's mountain stood almost as tall as she,
with twigs for trees and pebbles for animals. Elizabeth
was proud of her fine sand mountain.

The sun beat down, day after day, year after year,
on the earth mountain's sharp peaks. The wind howled
through its canyons.

Elizabeth's mountain baked in the afternoon heat.
The breeze loosened a few grains of sand and blew them
into Elizabeth's eyes and hair.

Countless rainstorms pounded the earth mountain.
The water seeped into its rocks, making them crumble,
then tumble into small streams.

An afternoon shower blew in suddenly and Elizabeth
watched as the water began to destroy the mountain
she had worked so hard to build. Her tears fell as freely
as the rain.

265

The small streams rushed together to become a
raging river. The river gouged a deep valley. It ground
the earth mountain's rough rocks into smooth pebbles.

Elizabeth could see the rain carving little valleys into her mountain. Tiny rivers carried the sand down the beach.

As the river flowed away from the earth mountain, it ground pebbles into sand and dumped the sand on a broad plain. Then it emptied into the sea.

Elizabeth saw the sand from her mountain spread
silently into small fans. She wiped away her tears.

In just a blink of earth time, the earth mountain
traded rocks for sand, jagged peaks for flat layers.

After a few minutes, the shower was over. Elizabeth's mountain was just a bump on the beach.

The thick and heavy layers of sand sank down, down, down into the earth until they were squeezed into layers of sandstone.

Elizabeth scooped up a handful of sand from one of the small fans on the beach. She smiled. It was wet and hard—just right. This time she hurried, for the sun was dropping in the sky.

The earth cracked and shifted again. Bending and
breaking, the sandstone layers slowly rose to become
a new mountain.

Elizabeth finished her new sand mountain. She
brushed sand off her hands, picked up her bucket, and
walked back up the beach.

Elizabeth is walking on the new earth mountain.
She steps carefully up the steep path from the beach.
When she stops to rest, she sees a smooth mound
of sand far below. It looks very small.

As she turns to leave, Elizabeth reaches out to touch the sandstone wall. Tiny grains of sand fall on her shoulders.

She brushes them off and watches them fall to the
ground, where they will stay for just a while...
in the sun, the wind and the rain.

Meet
Lisa Westberg Peters

Lisa Westberg Peters wanted to write a book for children that would explain geology and how mountains change over time.

"I was lucky enough to take some good geology courses and several unforgettable trips into the mountains," she said. Then she visited a mountain along the coast in Washington State and wrote the story that became *The Sun, the Wind and the Rain.*

Meet
Ted Rand

Ted Rand says the mountain painted on the cover of *The Sun, the Wind and the Rain* is Mt. Rainier in the Cascade Range in Washington State. He says that the beach and shoreline are very much like those on Puget Sound and along the Pacific Coast.

"I'd like to encourage young readers to draw and enjoy the fun of it. Drawing is a second language to me, and I hope it becomes that to you," Mr. Rand says.

Until I Saw the SEA

Until I saw the sea
I did not know
that wind
could wrinkle water so.

I never knew
that sun
could splinter a whole sea of blue.

Nor
did I know before,
a sea breathes in and out
upon a shore.

Lilian Moore

SPLISH.

The First Rains

Story by Peter Bonnici
Pictures by Lisa Kopper

The First Rains
by Peter Bonnici
illustrated by Lisa Kopper
Carolrhoda, 1985

Waiting for the first rains
is a sticky business.

SPLASH!

Water's Way
by Lisa Westberg Peters
illustrated by Ted Rand
Little, Brown, 1991

Water has a way
of changing.

LLAMA AND THE GREAT FLOOD

**A folk tale from Peru
by Ellen Alexander**

The Quechua people of Peru say that during ancient times, before the coming of the god Viracocha, this world reached a point at which it was about to end. A certain llama who was living high up in the Andes Mountains knew what was about to happen. He had a dream in which he saw the sea overflow and flood the whole world.

This dream upset the llama so that he could not eat.
He just walked around day after day, crying.

He acted this way even though his thoughtful
owner had given him a beautiful meadow to graze in.

The llama soon began growing thin, and his owner worried about him and then started to become angry.

Finally, the man threw an ear of corn at the llama and shouted, "Why don't you eat, you foolish animal?

"I allow you to graze in this beautiful meadow and you just stand there and cry!"

The llama looked at him and with great sadness in his voice answered in the man's language, "It is YOU who are the fool!

"Don't you know what is happening? Within five days the sea will overflow!

"Yes, it's true! The world will be destroyed!"

The man was frightened, and he cried out to the llama, "What will become of us? How can we save ourselves?"

The llama answered, "Let us go to the top of Willka Qutu. There we will be safe. But bring enough food for five days."

The man hurried home to tell his wife and gather food.
Then the family hurried off to the highest mountain.

When they reached the top of Willka Qutu, they saw gathered there animals of every kind.

There were more llamas, alpacas and guanacos, lions and foxes, tiny mice and great condors.

There were sheep, armadillos, colorful macaws, and every other type of animal that lived.

Almost at once the sea began to overflow and they all remained stranded there.

The sea covered all the other mountain peaks. Only the top of Willka Qutu remained above water.

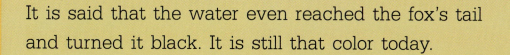

It is said that the water even reached the fox's tail and turned it black. It is still that color today.

At the end of five long, cold days, the sea went down again and everything began to dry out.

When the sea had gone all the way down,
it could be seen that there were no more
people or animals left in the world.

Except for those people and animals who were
watching all of this from the top of Willka Qutu.

Slowly, they began climbing down, until they stood once more in the meadows and valleys.

The people began rebuilding their house of stone, and the corral for their llama. They planted corn and potatoes.

Soon many new people and animals were born into
the world, and all were children of those on Willka Qutu.

The Andean people still speak of the great flood, and they believe that it was Willka Qutu and the llama who saved them from destruction.

Meet Ellen Alexander

Ellen Alexander has traveled to South America many times. She hikes or rides horseback into the mountains and sketches and paints what she sees.

Before she left on one trip, she read a myth about a llama who saved people from a great flood. Then she visited the mountain of Willka Qutu, where the people in the myth were saved, and decided to write a book about it.

"I want to show North American children the beauty that can be found in another culture," Ms. Alexander says.

WHAT floats?

"You can't mix oil with water," people say.
Why not?
Some liquids do not mix with other liquids.
Certain liquids float or sink in other liquids.
Some objects float or sink in liquids.
Try this experiment to see for yourself.

1 Pour the syrup into the bottom of the container.

You will need:
- Clear, tall container
- Syrup
- Cooking oil
- Water with red food coloring
- Rubbing alcohol with blue food coloring
- Grape
- Cork
- Plastic building block

2 Pour in the same amount of cooking oil. It floats on the syrup.

3 Now add the same amount of water. It sinks through the oil but floats on the syrup.

4 Finally, add the same amount of rubbing alcohol, the lightest liquid. It floats on the oil.

5 Now add the plastic building block, the cork and the grape in the container.

That was my secret project.

I had a bottle with a cork. I had paper and a ballpoint pen. I wrote a message: *Whoever finds this bottle, please write or call me and tell me where you found it.*

I put down my address and phone number. Then I corked the bottle and carried it down to the river.

I threw the bottle as far out as I could. It splashed, bobbed up and floated. I watched it go out of sight.

"You know," my father said, "there's something we could do. We could walk out on the bridge. And if you wanted, you could send a new message. Your bottle would have a good chance from there. It's past the curve in the river."

I thought about it. I decided to do it. And I told my father.

"You know," he said, "if you don't mind my advice—put something special about yourself in the bottle, for the person who finds it."

"Why?" I asked.

"It'll give the wind and the water something special to carry. If you send something you care about, it might bring you luck."

I was working on my new message. And then I thought about Huey and Gloria. I thought how they might want to send bottles too. It didn't seem so important anymore that I be the only one to do it.

And that's what we did. We all got new bottles, and we put something special in each one. We each made a picture of ourselves for our bottle.

And in his, Huey put his favorite joke:
Where does a hamburger go on New Year's Eve?
To a meat ball.

Anytime you do a big thing, it's good to make wishes."

We did.

I don't know what Huey or Gloria wished. I wished our bottles would sail along together. I wished they wouldn't get trapped in seaweed or ice, or hit rocks. I wished we'd make new friends on the other side of the world. I wished we'd go to meet them someday.

"Ready?" my father said.

Together we threw our bottles over the side. They made a tiny splash. They looked very small, but we could see them starting toward the ocean.

They were like Columbus's ships. I hoped they'd stay together a long, long time.

Meet Ann Cameron

"A book is like a message in a bottle that an author throws out to sea: you never know whom it might reach, or how much it might mean to them."

The idea for stories about Julian, his little brother Huey, and his best friend Gloria came from stories a friend named Julian told Ms. Cameron about his childhood.

Ann Cameron tells of how much she loved watching her grandfather heat bars of iron in his forge. The heavy bars of iron turned red hot and then white hot over the coals. Sparks flew as he hammered them into beautiful and useful things.

"Sometimes I feel like him as my mind hammers at the cold, stiff material of words," Ms. Cameron writes.

Meet Ann Strugnell

Ann Strugnell has illustrated *The Stories Julian Tells; More Stories Julian Tells;* and *Julian, Dream Doctor.*

Ms. Strugnell studied sculpture before beginning to illustrate children's books. She lives in London, England, with her husband and two sons.

River Winding

Rain falling, what things do you grow?
Snow melting, where do you go?
Wind blowing, what trees do you know?
River winding, where do you flow?

Charlotte Zolotow

The Tide in the River

The tide in the river,
The tide in the river,
The tide in the river runs deep,
I saw a shiver
Pass over the river
As the tide turned in its sleep.

Eleanor Farjeon

INFORMATION ILLUSTRATED

A GUIDE TO SKILLS AND INFORMATION SOURCES THAT GO WITH THE STORIES YOU ARE READING!

CONTENTS

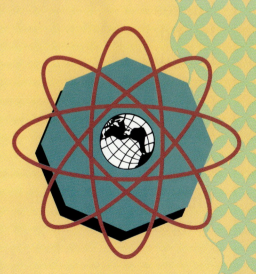

CHARTS AND TABLES

SOME DIFFERENT KINDS OF PENGUINS

Name	Where Found	Habitat	Height	Usual Number of Eggs
Emperor Penguin	Antarctica	ocean and pack ice	48 inches (122 cm)	1
Chinstrap Penguin	Antarctica and polar islands	coastal waters	30 inches (75 cm)	2
Adélie Penguin	Antarctica and polar islands	coastal waters	30 inches (75 cm)	2
Snares Island Penguin	New Zealand	coastal waters	29 inches (73 cm)	2
Galápagos Penguin	Galápagos Islands	coastal waters	20 inches (50 cm)	2
Little Penguin	Australia, New Zealand, and nearby islands	coastal waters	16 inches (40 cm)	2

CHARTS AND TABLES

"MESSAGE" MACHINES
IN OUR TOWN'S SCHOOLS

School	Telephones	Copying Machines	Television Sets	FAX Machines
Central School	7	3	4	1
Grant School	10	4	3	1
North School	8	4	5	0
West School	9	5	7	1
Wood School	4	1	2	0

DIAGRAMS

A Soccer Field

75 yards

20 yards

6 yds

Corner Flag

6 yds

Goal Area

18 yds

6 yds

6 yds

Penalty Area

4 yds

Penalty Arc

Touch Line

B O U N D S

Center Spot

Center Line

20 yards

Center Circle

Center Circle

B O U N D S

O U T O F

Touch Line

Penalty Kick Spot

● player on kicking (defensive) team

Corner

Goal Line

Goal Area

18 yds

8 yds

18 yds

Goal

44 yards

115 yards

8ft

Goal (side view)

French Cricket

You will need:
- A soft ball
- A cricket bat, or a flat piece of wood, or a tennis racket

French Cricket is a game for two or more players.
It can be played at the beach, in the park, or on the playground.

1 One player is the batter. All the other players are bowlers.

2 The bowlers try to hit the batter below the knees with the ball.

3 The batter tries to stop the ball from hitting him or her by using the bat.

4 The batter is out if the ball hits his or her legs below the knees, or if a bowler catches the ball after the batter has hit it.

5 The batter makes points by scoring a run. This can be done only when no bowler is holding the ball. To score a run, the batter passes the bat around his or her body, changing it from one hand to the other. Each time the batter passes the bat this way counts as one run.

6 When the batter is out, he or she becomes a bowler, and another player becomes the batter.

7 The winner is the player with the most runs after everyone has had a chance at bat.

DIRECTIONS

SIGN LANGUAGE

The hand signals for the letters of the alphabet in one system of sign language are shown below. When using these signals to "talk" with someone, remember to:

1. Keep your hand where the person you are "talking" to can see it.

2. Make your signals clear and precise.

3. Mark breaks between words by snapping the fingers or by quickly putting both hands together, separating them, and jerking them downward.

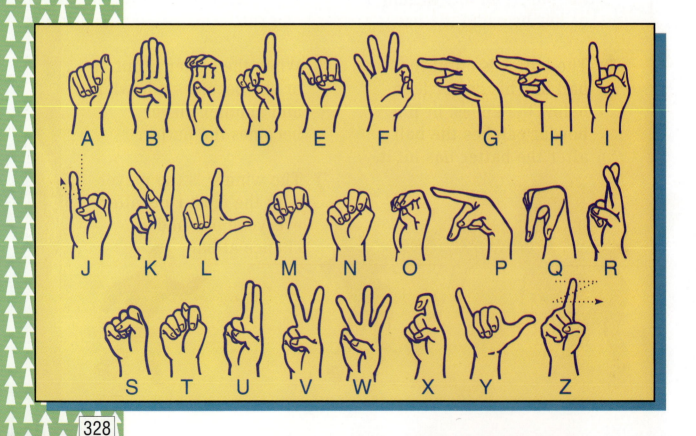

FORMS

Fun • Informative • Creative

SCIENCE & EARTH

A Magazine For Children

── ORDER FORM ──

Please Print

NAME ELIZABETH RILEY

ADDRESS 431 TUPELO STREET

CITY PRESTON **STATE** KANSAS **ZIP** 00000

COUNTRY U.S.A.

TELEPHONE (9 / 1 / 3) 5 5 5 — 7 2 9 9

DATE OF BIRTH APRIL 4 1988
MONTH   DAY   YEAR

- ☐ 1 YEAR (8 ISSUES) $12.00
- ☑ 2 YEARS (16 ISSUES) $20.00

- ☑ PAYMENT ENCLOSED ☐ BILL ME

Elizabeth Riley
Signature

Ann Riley
Signature of Parent or Guardian
(Required if under 18)

DATE: 7 / 4 / 93
MONTH / DAY / YEAR

Return to: **SCIENCE AND EARTH**
P.O. BOX 90
MONTGOMERY, WA 00000

329

GRAPHS

Soccer Goals Scored This Season

Player	⚽ = 1 Goal
Abby	⚽⚽⚽⚽⚽⚽⚽⚽⚽
Eric	⚽⚽⚽⚽
Joan	⚽⚽⚽⚽⚽⚽
Jonathan	⚽⚽⚽
Moira	⚽⚽⚽⚽⚽⚽⚽⚽
Toby	⚽⚽⚽⚽⚽⚽⚽

Games Our School Won This Year

□ = 1 Game

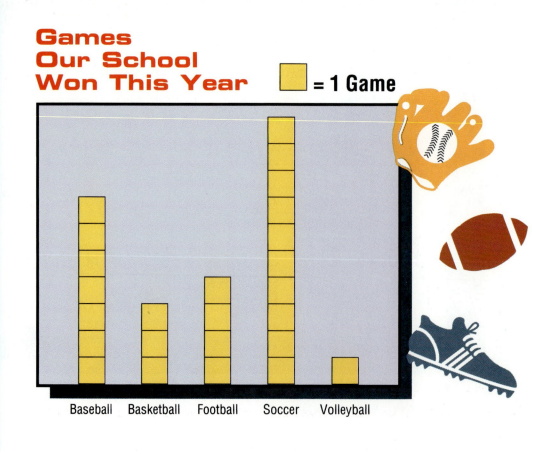

Baseball   Basketball   Football   Soccer   Volleyball

MAPS

SOUTH AMERICA
INCA LANDS
KEY
- Inca lands
- - - - Modern boundary
- (Peru) Modern country

(Colombia)

(Ecuador)

S O U T H

A M E R I C A

(Peru)

(Bolivia)

PACIFIC

OCEAN

(Chile) (Argentina)

ATLANTIC

OCEAN

N
W E
S

PACIFIC

OCEAN

COLOMBIA

⊛ Quito

ECUADOR

A N D E S   M O U N T A I N S

Putumayo

Amazon

Ucayali

Javarí

BRAZIL

PERU

Lima ⊛

Lake
Titicaca

BOLIVIA

⊛ La Paz
Lake
Poopó

CHILE

N
W E
S

PERU: Landforms
KEY
- Mountains
- Hills
- Plains
- ⊛ National capital
- ▬ National boundary
- 〜 River

Glos

This glossary can help you to find out the meanings of words in this book that you may not know.

The words are in alphabetical order. Guide words tell you the first and last words on the page.

Glossary

Glossary entries are based on entries in *The Macmillan/McGraw-Hill Primary Dictionary* and *The Macmillan/McGraw-Hill School Dictionary 1.*

bundle

A **bundle** is a number of things tied or wrapped together. Please put that **bundle** of newspapers in the box. ▲ **bundles.**

canyon

A **canyon** is a deep valley with very high, steep sides. Looking down into a **canyon** is an awesome sight. ▲ **canyons.**

careless

Careless means that you are not thinking about what you are doing. Lee was **careless** and spilled the milk.

cartwheel

A **cartwheel** is a kind of sideways jump from your feet to your hands and back again. Lisa learned to do **cartwheels** in gym class. ▲ **cartwheels.**

caterpillar

A **caterpillar** is an insect that looks like a worm with fur. **Caterpillars** come from eggs and will become butterflies. Did you ever hold a **caterpillar** in your hand? It tickles! ▲ **caterpillars.**

chicken pox

Chicken pox is a kind of illness in which the person gets a fever and rash. It is easily passed from one person to another. The twins got **chicken pox** at just about the same time.

China

China is a large country in eastern Asia. More people live in China than in any other country in the world. Lin's grandfather was born in **China.**

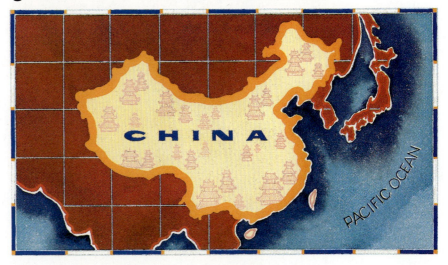

chive

Chive is a plant related to the onion and used to add to food for flavor. **Chives** have an onion flavor. My mom likes cream cheese and **chive** sandwiches. ▲ **chives.**

condor

A **condor** is a large bird with a hooked bill and a head and neck without feathers. Peter once saw a **condor** when he was hiking in the mountains of California. ▲ **condors.**

continent

A **continent** is one of seven large land areas on the earth. We live on the **continent** of North America.
▲ **continents.**

corral

A **corral** is an area with a fence around it. A **corral** is used to keep cattle, horses, and other animals in one place.
▲ **corrals.**

countless

Countless means too many to be counted. There are **countless** stars in the sky.

creek

A **creek** is a small stream. Josie learned how to fish in a **creek.** ▲ **creeks.**

crumble

Crumble means to break into small pieces. The muffin **crumbled** when I tried to butter it. ▲ **crumbled, crumbling.**

cushion

A **cushion** is a pillow or soft pad to sit, lie, or rest on. Our couch has three **cushions** on the seat. ▲ **cushions.**

D

damage

Damage means to harm or injure. The wind **damaged** the fence around our house. ▲ **damaged, damaging.**

destroy

Destroy means to ruin completely. A big wave **destroyed** our sand castle. ▲ **destroyed, destroying.**

diamond

A **diamond** is a hard, clean, shiny stone. Some rings have **diamonds** in them. ▲ **diamonds.**

dummy

A **dummy** is something that is made to look like something else that is real. When you look at the **dummy** of a newspaper, you can tell how it will look after it is printed. ▲ **dummies.**

Eskimo

An **Eskimo** is a member of a people living in Alaska, northern Canada, and other very cold regions. **Eskimos** spend many months each year in very cold weather.
▲ **Eskimos.**

exhaust

Exhaust means to make very weak or tired. The long hike in hot weather **exhausted** us. ▲ **exhausted, exhausting.**

familiar

When something is **familiar,** it is often seen or heard. Cows are a **familiar** sight on a farm.

footprint

A **footprint** is a mark made by a foot or shoe. We could see the **footprints** of the birds on the wet sand. ▲ **footprints.**

foreign

Foreign means outside a person's own country. Have you ever visited any **foreign** countries?

France

France is a country in western Europe. **France** is famous for its delicious food.

G

gleam

Gleam means to shine or glow. The new car **gleamed** in the sunlight. ▲ **gleamed, gleaming.**

guanaco

A **guanaco** is a long-legged wild animal of South America that looks something like a llama. It is hard to tell the difference between a **guanaco** and a llama. ▲ **guanacos.**

H

Hawaii

Hawaii is a state of the United States made up of a group of islands in the Pacific Ocean. The beaches in **Hawaii** have very big waves.

hedge

A **hedge** is a row of shrubs or small trees planted close together. Mom trimmed the **hedge** around our house. ▲ **hedges.**

India

India is a country in southern Asia. Annar's mother was born in **India.**

island

An **island** is a body of land that is surrounded on all sides by water. Something that looks like an island and is completely surrounded by something else is also called an **island.** We waited on the **island** before crossing the street. ▲ **islands.**

jangle

Jangle means to make a harsh or unpleasant sound. The janitor **jangled** a bunch of keys. ▲ **jangled, jangling.**

kinfolk

Kinfolk are a person's relatives or family. All of my **kinfolk** live in the same city.

layer

Layer is one thickness of material on or over something. A **layer** of dust covered the table. ▲ **layers.**

macaw

A **macaw** is a large, brightly colored parrot. A **macaw** can repeat many words that it hears. ▲ **macaws.**

medicine

Medicine is something we take when we are sick to help us get well. When Jane had the flu, her mother gave her **medicine** twice a day. ▲ **medicines.**

N

newsstand

A **newsstand** is a stand where newspapers and magazines are sold. Dad buys a newspaper at the same **newsstand** every day. ▲ **newsstands.**

noble

Noble means having high rank or a title. The prince and princess come from **noble** families. ▲ **nobler, noblest.**

North Pole

The **North Pole** is the point on earth that is the farthest north. Can you find the **North Pole** on a globe?

O

out-of-bounds

In sports, **out-of-bounds** means outside the allowed area of play. Patty kicked the soccer ball really far, but it was **out-of-bounds.**

peak

A **peak** is the point at the top of a mountain. We took a picture of the **peaks** covered with snow. ▲ **peaks.**

plain

A **plain** is an area of flat or almost flat land. Buffaloes used to roam the Western **plains.** ▲ **plains.**

position

A **position** is the place where a person or thing is. From my **position** at the window, I could see the whole parade. ▲ **positions.**

pursuit

Pursuit means following someone or something in order to catch up to it. Patty was in **pursuit** of the ball that had gone over her head. ▲ **pursuits.**

quit

Quit means to stop doing something. Joe **quit** swimming when he got too cold. ▲ **quit** or **quitted, quitting.**

rage

Rage means to act or move with great force or violence. The storm **raged** along the coast. ▲ **raged, raging.**

realize

Realize means to understand completely. I didn't **realize** how late it was. ▲ **realized, realizing.**

reduce

Reduce means to make or become less or smaller in size, number, or degree. Drivers should **reduce** their speed if the road is slippery. ▲ **reduced, reducing.**

rescue

Rescue means to save or free. Carlos **rescued** the kitten from the tree.
▲ **rescued, rescuing.**

Rio de Janeiro

Rio de Janeiro is a city in the country of Brazil. Carnival is a big festival held in **Rio de Janeiro** every year.

satellite

A **satellite** is a spacecraft that moves in an orbit around the earth, the moon, or other bodies in space. **Satellites** are used to forecast the weather, to relay radio, telephone, and television communications, and to provide information about conditions in space. The **satellite** sends the latest news stories to the television station.
▲ **satellites.**

seaweed

Seaweed is a plant that grows in the sea. **Seaweed** washed up on the beach after the storm. ▲ **seaweeds.**

seep

Seep means to flow or spread slowly. Water **seeped** into the ground after the rain. ▲ **seeped, seeping.**

servant

A **servant** is a person hired to do personal or household work for others. Some rich people hire **servants** to do work around their houses. ▲ **servants.**

snack

A **snack** is a small amount of food or drink eaten between meals. Apples are Jack's favorite **snack.** ▲ **snacks.**

sparkle

Sparkle means to shine in quick, bright flashes. The sun **sparkled** on the water. ▲ **sparkled, sparkling.**

squeal

Squeal means to make a loud, shrill cry or sound. The child **squealed** with delight when she stepped in the mud. ▲ **squealed, squealing.**

squeegee

A **squeegee** is a tool that makes a kind of squeaky sound and that is used to wipe off or spread liquid. The **squeegee** made a squeaky sound when we used it on our windshield. ▲ **squeegees.**

squiggle

A **squiggle** is a small, wiggly mark.

My little sister Meg makes **squiggles** when she writes her name. ▲ **squiggles.**

stout

Stout means thick and heavy or fat. The baseball player was strong and **stout.** ▲ **stouter, stoutest.**

strand

Strand means to leave in a helpless position. We were **stranded** on a country road when our car broke down.
▲ **stranded, stranding.**

subscribe

Subscribe means to agree to receive and pay for. The library **subscribes** to magazines and newspapers.
▲ **subscribed, subscribing.**

supervisor

A **supervisor** is a person who watches over and directs the work of other people. ▲ **supervisors.**

swirl

Swirl means to move around and around. The wind **swirled** the dry leaves into the ditch. ▲ **swirled, swirling.**

swollen

Something is **swollen** when it has grown in size. The river was **swollen** after the heavy rainstorm.

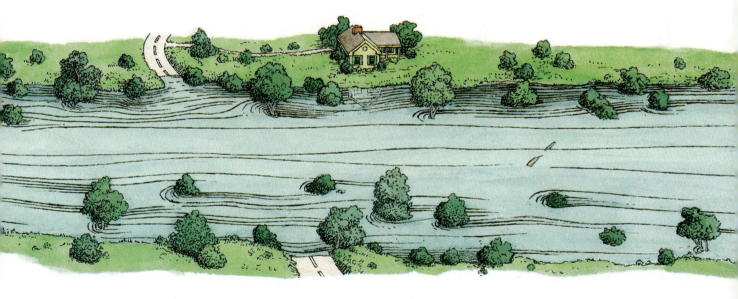

syndicate

A **syndicate** is an organization that sells articles, stories, and comic strips to a number of newspapers. The **syndicate** sold the story to 120 newspapers. ▲ **syndicates.**

tackle

Tackle means to stop or bring to the ground. The farmer **tackled** the pig as it ran away. ▲ **tackled, tackling.**

teammate

A **teammate** is a person who is a member of the same team. Many of my basketball **teammates** have become my friends. ▲ **teammates.**

trim

Trim means to cut away or remove parts to make something neat and orderly. Please **trim** the bush evenly. ▲ **trimmed, trimming.**

tumble

Tumble means to fall in a helpless or clumsy way. Our puppy **tumbled** down the stairs when it was going after the ball. ▲ **tumbled, tumbling.**

U

uncle

Your **uncle** is your father's brother or your mother's brother. Your aunt's husband is also your **uncle**. My **Uncle** Pete is teaching me how to play chess. ▲ **uncles.**

V

vibrate

Vibrate means to move or cause to move quickly back and forth or up and down. The strings of a guitar **vibrate** when they are strummed. ▲ **vibrated, vibrating.**

Vietnam

Vietnam is a country in southeastern Asia. The new boy in our class is from **Vietnam.**

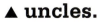

warning

A **warning** is a statement that tells beforehand about a danger or a possible bad result. The **warning** on the label said the bottle contained poison.
▲ **warnings.**

whisper

Whisper means to speak in a very quiet voice. The teacher asked the students to **whisper** when they shared their stories.
▲ **whispered, whispering.**